The Big Book of Puzzles and Paradoxes

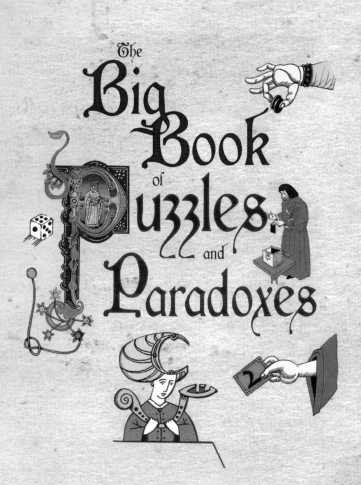

© Marabout (Hachette Livre) 2007

This 2009 edition published by Metro Books,
by arrangement with Carlton Books Limited

English translation by Barry Goodman

Metro Books
122 Fifth Avenue
New York, NY 10011

ISBN 978-1-4351-2117-1

Printed and bound in China

1 3 5 7 9 10 8 6 4 2

The Big Book of Puzzles and Paradoxes

Fabrice Mazza

Illustrated by Ivan Sigg

METRO BOOKS
NEW YORK

CONTENTS

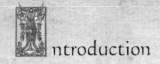ntroduction

Dear reader:

If the Sphinx had not asked a riddle of travellers to Thebes and had simply been happy to eat everyone who appeared in front of her, would the world have been a different place?

Without a doubt. In fact we all need to question and we need uncertainty, just as we need singularity and astonishment. And although certain enigmas may well be unsolvable, those we have gathered together in this book are all answered in the second half of it.

But it is not only finding the answer that counts - and only look them up as a last resort - but the path you follow to get to it, a path that is different and depends upon every individual's insight, cultural background, imagination and so on.

There is no universal method to solving problems but it is always helpful to think off the beaten track and use your intuition and wisdom to help you get through. And in the way that life is full of surprises, in these pages you'll learn how to calculate π as well as how to peel an egg without touching it!

Remember also that the pleasure you derive from solving an enigma is proportional to the initial difficulty that you encountered, and that a problem shared is not always a problem solved… And obviously, just because you are searching by yourself does not mean that you are searching alone…

Happy reading and happy puzzling!

DIVINATION

At a banquet in honour of King Arthur, a conjuror amazed the gathering with this trick: he invited a courtier to draw a card from a deck of thirty-two and declared that he would be able to guess the card correctly.

He asked the courtier a number of questions as follows:

-- Does the card have a number?

-- Yes.

-- Is it an even number?

-- Yes.

-- Is it the number 8?

-- No.

-- Is the suit black?

-- Yes.

-- Is it a club?

-- No.

What card did the courtier hold in his hand?

Solution p. 158

AGIC KNOT

A juggler holds a rope with one end in each hand.

How can he make a knot in the rope without letting go?

APPLES

While out picking fruit, a farmer's wife with eight children only managed to collect five apples. However, she was able to share the fruit equally among all her children.

How did she do this?

Solution p. 160

YSTERIOUS PURCHASE

Godefroy de Bouillon meets a tinker, and the conversation
goes thus:

-- What does 1 cost?
-- That would be 3 groats.
-- And 10?
-- 6 groats.
-- And 200?
-- 9 groats.

What is Godefroy de
Bouillon shopping for?

TRAVELS

Marco Fulcanelli has travelled extensively.

On his first trip, he met Marianne Argento. On the second,
he fell in love with Violaine Lerouge.
On the third, he married Pauline Leprince.
And finally, on the fourth, he made Karima Abdi his mistress.

On which of his trips did he
die of a serious illness?

Solution p. 162

# CROSSING OUT

As part of his studies in algebra, the mathematician Leonardo Fibonacci takes a sheet of parchment and writes down all the numbers from 1 to 30 inclusive.

He then crosses out various numbers, until he is left with only whole numbers that are not double any other number on the sheet.

What are the numbers that are left?

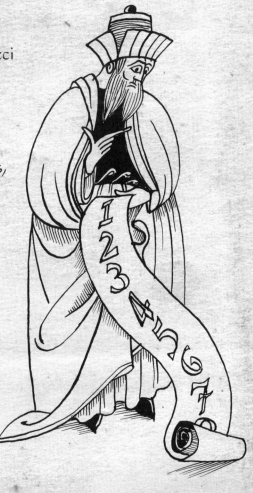

ILLUSION

Something strange is going on in this armoury ...
Which window frame is taller: A or B?

Solution p. 164

INE WINE

On returning to camp, a warrior knight is preparing to celebrate victory in the latest battle. He wants to drink a toast to his soldiers and decides to open a bottle of wine. Unfortunately, he has no corkscrew and he is in the middle of the forest!

How can he open the bottle with the help of nothing more than his cloak?

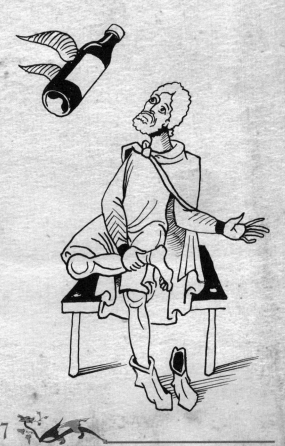

A SURPRISING SQUARE

Why is the square of 111,111,111 so surprising?

$$111\ 111\ 111^2 = ?$$

Solution p. 166

UP THE GREAT LADDER

A workman on the building site of Bourges Cathedral is standing on the middle rung of a ladder. He needs to climb to the top in order to reach the bell-tower. He climbs three rungs but, suddenly struck with vertigo, descends five rungs. Gathering his courage, the workman decides to go up again and this time manages seven rungs. After stopping to catch his breath, he climbs the last six rungs and reaches the bell-tower.

How many rungs does the ladder have?

Solution p. 167

 RIGAMI

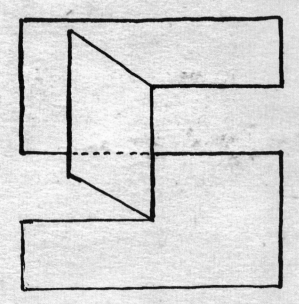

How can you create this origami figure with one simple sheet of paper, and without using glue?

Solution p. 168

 HAT AM I?

When I'm going, it doesn't mean I'm moving.
I can stop even though I don't go anywhere.
I don't have any arms but I do have hands.

What am I?

 ABYRINTH

At the Battle of Roncevaux, Roland finds himself cut off from the rest of his troops. Starting from A, how can he get to B in less than 30 seconds?

Solution p. 170

TANDARD

This heraldic standard is made up of 16 squares arranged in 4 boxes:

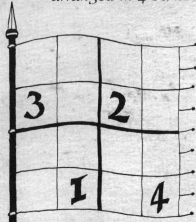

Can you complete the grid, in less than three minutes, in such a way that the numbers 1 to 4 appear just once in each box, and that each number appears only once in each row and column?

IGH TIDE

At low tide, on a ship's ladder fixed at the top to the side of the boat, there are 17 rungs showing above the water line. These rungs are 6 inches (15cm) apart, and the sea is rising at a rate of 1 ft (30 cm) an hour.

After an hour and a half in a rising tide, how many rungs will be above the water line?

Solution p. 172

PYRAMID OF ODD NUMBERS

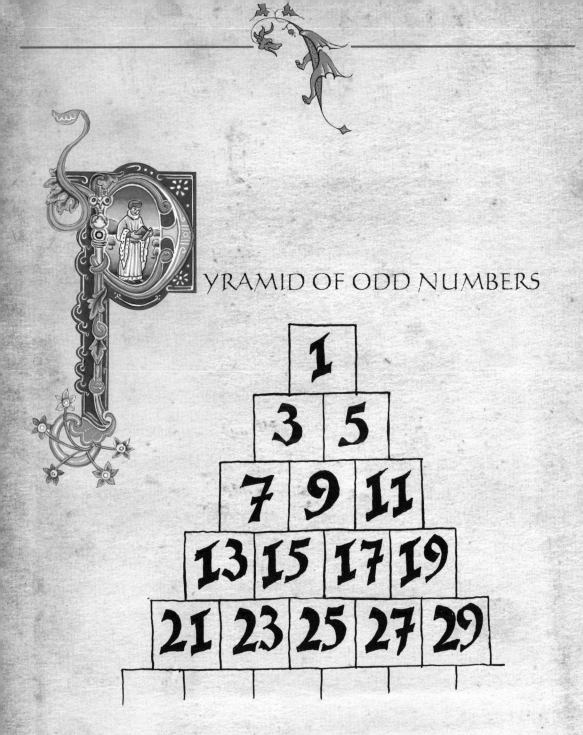

What is the sum of the numbers on the fifteenth line of this pyramid?

WINTER GARDEN

It has been snowing heavily. Baudouin goes outdoors and notices that there is twice as much snow in his garden as in his neighbour Gaël's. However, he is not at all surprised. Why?

Solution p. 174

WHAT AM I?

I am the duration of 9,192,631,770 periods of the radiation corresponding to the transition between the two hyperfine levels of the ground state of the caesium 133 atom.

What am I?

 IGNS FOR A HUNDRED

Without changing the order, insert an arithmetical symbol between each number so that the total adds up to 100.

$$1\ 2\ 3\ 4\ 5\ 6\ 7\ 8\ 9 = 100$$

Solution p. 176

 IGNS WITH FIVE

Using what arithmetical symbols is it possible to make 100 using the number 5 five times?

# ITORI

Shade in certain squares so that:
-- the same number does not appear in any row or column more than once;
-- no two shaded squares are adjacent;
-- the unshaded squares are connected to each other (it must be possible to move from one unshaded square to another horizontally or vertically).

4	8	1	6	3	2	5	7
3	6	7	2	1	6	5	4
2	3	4	8	2	8	6	1
4	1	6	5	7	7	3	5
7	2	3	1	8	5	1	2
3	5	6	7	3	1	8	4
6	4	2	3	5	4	7	8
8	7	1	4	2	3	5	6

Solution p. 178

OUR QUEENS

On this chessboard, how should you place four queens so that the opposing king is always in check, whatever its position on the board?

	a	b	c	d	e	f	g	h	i	j	k	l
1												
2												
3												
4												
5												

Reminder: the queen can move along any line vertically or horizontally, as well as diagonally.

Solution p. 179

PRISONERS

Two prisoners are attached to each other in the following way:

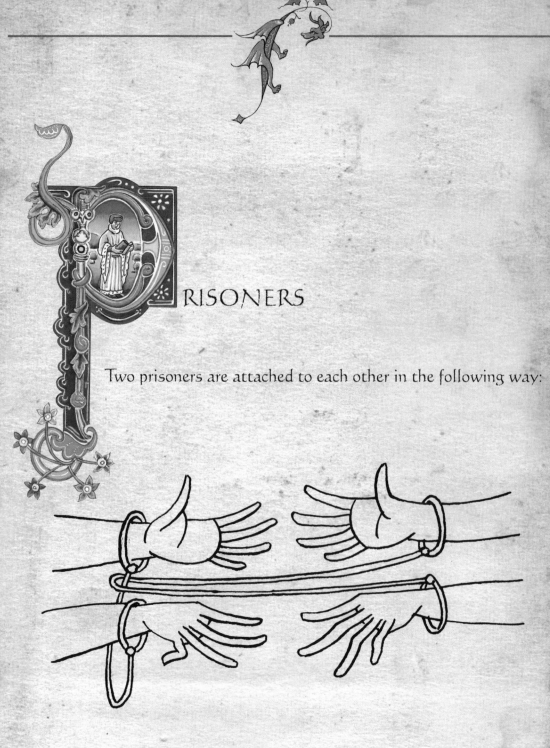

How can they free themselves without cutting the rope?

Solution p. 180

GREEDY WHIM

Dame Berthe has seven children and a tin containing seven biscuits.

Each child wants a biscuit but they also want Dame Berthe to leave one in the tin!

How can she satisfy her whimsical brood?

 IX TRIANGLES

A master glazier is working out the composition of a stained-glass window with the help of some matches. Here is his problem: how can he get six identical triangles by removing just three matches?

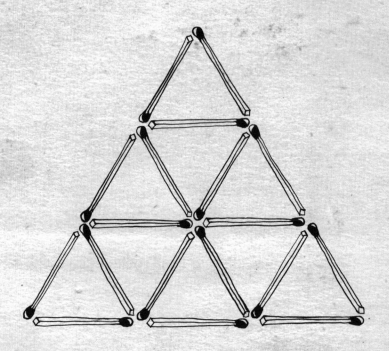

Solution p. 182

 OUR TRIANGLES

And now, how can he get four identical triangles to appear just by taking away four matches?

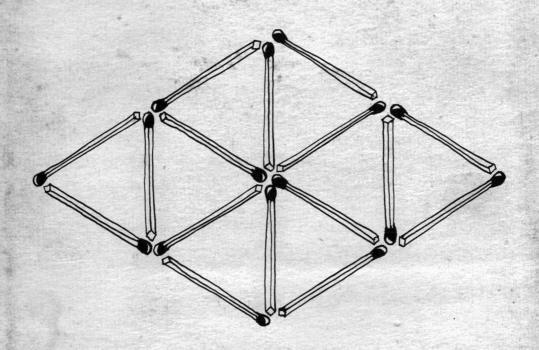

 EVENTEEN STICKS

Two knights, Yvain and Galahad, are arguing over who might pay court to a lady. To settle the argument, the king sits them at a table on which he places 17 sticks.

Taking turns, the knights may pick up one, two or three sticks. The king decrees that whoever picks up the last stick must yield to the other.

What strategy should Yvain adopt to be sure of winning?

Solution p. 184

CROUBADOURS

Three friends, Martin, Éberulf and Léandre, make up a group of minstrels. Two out of the three play the lute, two the bagpipes and two the hurdy-gurdy.

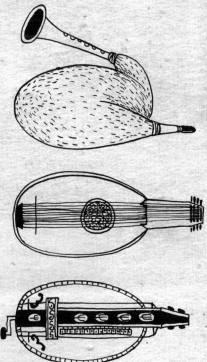

The one who doesn't play the hurdy-gurdy doesn't play the bagpipes either, and the one who doesn't play the bagpipes doesn't play the lute.

Which instruments does each minstrel play?

Solution p. 185

LETTER FOR A NUMBER

Replace the letters A, B, C, D, and E with the numbers 1, 2, 3, 4 and 5 so that this calculation works.

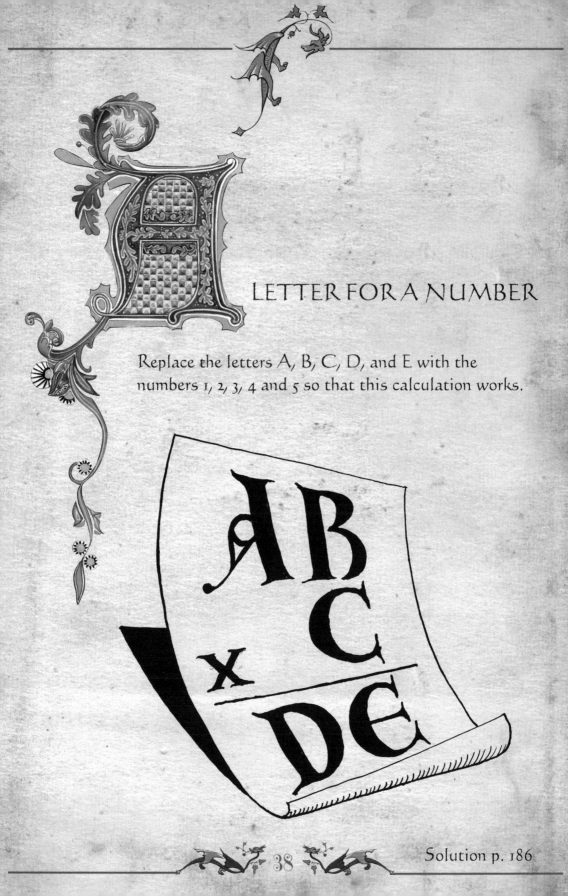

$$\begin{array}{r} AB \\ \times\ C \\ \hline DE \end{array}$$

Solution p. 186

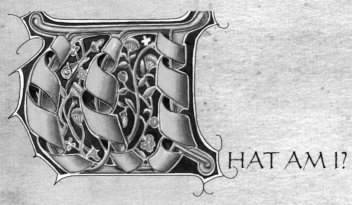HAT AM I?

He who makes me sells me, he who buys me does not use me and he who does use me isn't aware of it.

What am I?

 N EQUAL PARTS

How can this shield be
divided into four equal parts?

And this coat of arms into
five identical parts?

Solution p. 188

CARD CONUNDRUM

A conjuror takes four cards from a tarot deck and produces a knave, a queen, a king and an ace. Can you work out their suits and the way they are laid out given the following information?

1st clue: the spade is next to the diamond.

2nd clue: the club is immediately to the left of either the king or the queen.

3rd clue: the king is immediately to the right of a red card.

4th clue: the card furthest to the right is not a heart.

5th clue: one of the two middle cards is the knave.

6th clue: the king and the queen are not next to each other.

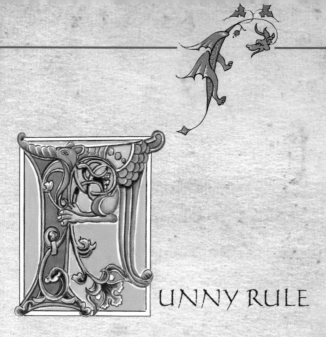

FUNNY RULE

According to a strange rule, 4 is half of 9, 6 is half of 11 and 7 is half of 12.

So what is half of 13?

Solution p. 190

TURNING COINS

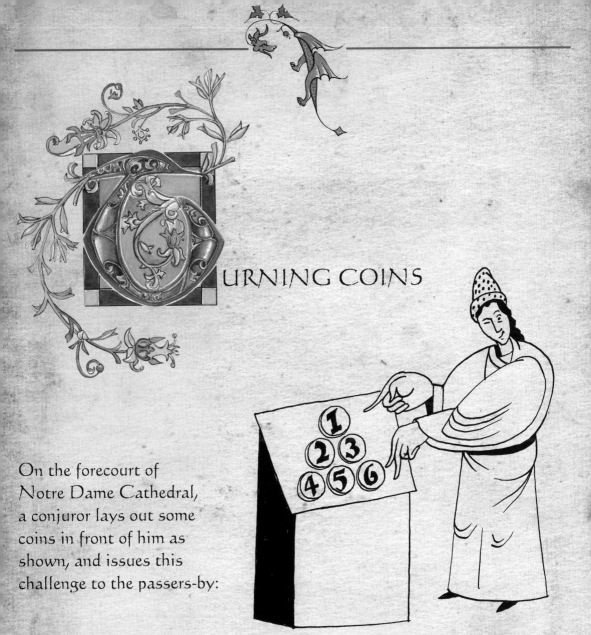

On the forecourt of Notre Dame Cathedral, a conjuror lays out some coins in front of him as shown, and issues this challenge to the passers-by:

"Who can form these coins into a circle in just four moves, only moving one coin at a time and without causing any of the others to move, and in such a way that any coin that has been moved, touches two other coins?"

HICKENS

Landry the farmer owns 32 chickens, which he keeps in an enclosure as shown below:

The farmer has organised his fowls in such a way that the total number of chickens in rows 1 and 3, as well as in columns A and C, equals 12. His business prospers and he therefore decides to buy a dozen more chickens. As the owner now of forty-four birds, he wonders if his enclosure will still be able to accommodate 12 chickens in rows 1 and 3 and columns A and C, or if he will have to build a new one.

Can you help Landry?

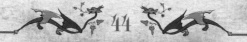

Solution p. 192

OUNTAIN

Before Mount Everest was discovered, what was the highest mountain in the world?

PAYMENT

Lords Childebert and Sigismond have collected the taxes due on their lands and each has as much money as the other.

How many groats must Childebert give Sigismond for Sigismond to end up with 1,000 groats more than him?

Solution p. 194

XCAVATION

How much earth is contained in a hole 1 yard (1m) deep, 1 foot (30cm) wide and 1 foot (30cm) long?

 AGIC FIGURE

On this shield, replace the black dots with the numbers 1 to 19 so that the sum of each line equals 38.

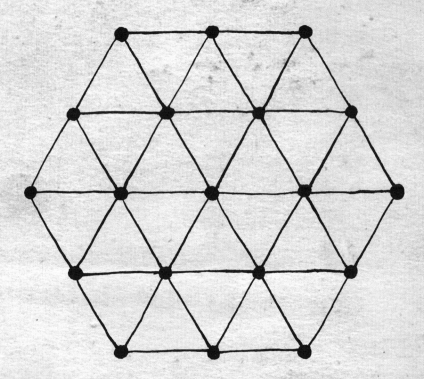

Solution p. 196

 ENEALOGY

Gondemar is the son of Brunehaut.
Landéric is Gondemar's brother.
Brunehaut is the daughter of Liébault.

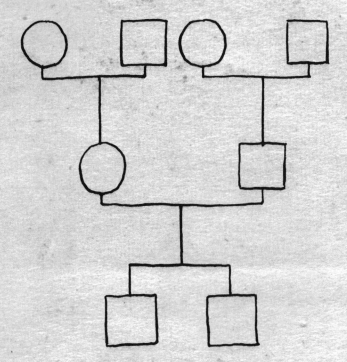

Who is Landéric's grandfather?

ONNECTIONS

A scribe working on an illuminated manuscript is trying to work out the best way to join the dots to create the shape of an envelope, but without lifting his pen from the parchment.

Can you help him?

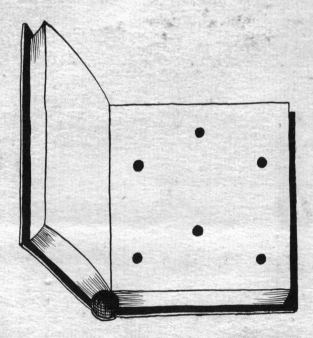

Solution p. 198

 RUEL DILEMMA

A guilty thief who has been put to the rack is granted one last favour by his executioner: he may nominate the manner of his death. He must choose from being:

-- crushed under the weight of a five-ton stone;
-- thrown into a pit of lions who have not eaten for five months;
-- boiled in oil for seven days and seven nights;
-- poisoned by five scorpions, ten tarantulas and twenty serpents;
-- decapitated at full moon;
-- or eaten alive by a tribe of cannibals.

Which of these should he choose?

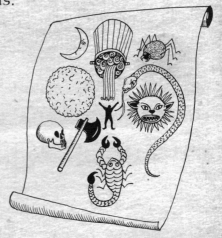

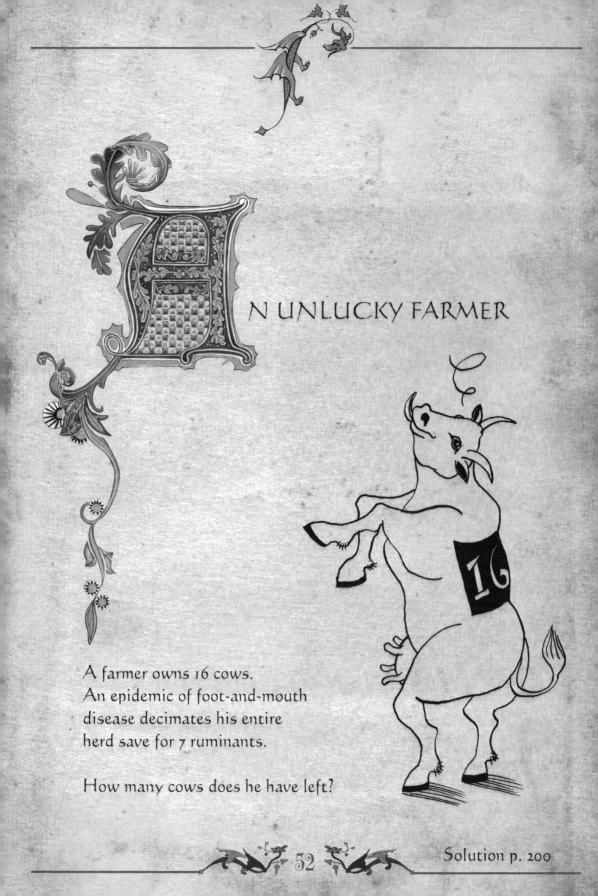

An unlucky farmer

A farmer owns 16 cows.
An epidemic of foot-and-mouth
disease decimates his entire
herd save for 7 ruminants.

How many cows does he have left?

Solution p. 200

DRAINS

Why are manhole covers always round?

FOLDS

Can a sheet of parchment one tenth of an inch thick, be folded in half 20 times?

Solution p. 202

ORE FOLDS

Assuming it were possible, how thick would the sheet of parchment be after it had been folded in half 20 times? And 60 times?

Solution p. 203

RAKING LEAVES

Two serfs are busy raking up the dead lesaves in the castle's courtyard: one makes three piles of leaves while the other makes seven.

When they've finished and put the fruits of their labour together, how many piles will they have?

Solution p. 204

DIVISIONS

Divide this orchard into four parts so that each part is the same size and the same shape, and has the same number of fruit trees:

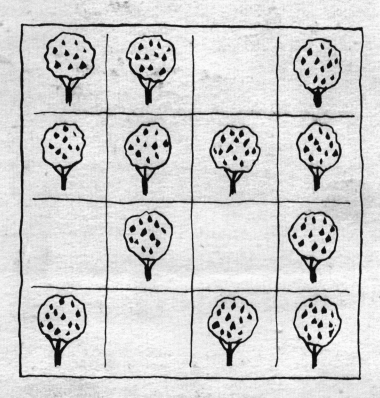

 OMPULSIVE LIAR

Dame Frénégonde tells her friends that her grandmother is only five years older than her mother, yet she is not lying.

How can this be?

Solution p. 206

THE COLUMN OF NUMBERS

A monk commits a breach of the rules by speaking during supper. As his penance, he has to solve a riddle posed by the Prior:

"Write down two numbers that are lower than 10, add them up and put the total underneath. Continue in this way, adding the last two numbers as you go, and stop when your column contains ten numbers. Tell me the sixth number on your list, and I shall be able to tell you the sum of all the numbers in the column.

How do I do it?"

Can you help the errant monk?

AN ABUNDANCE OF SQUARES

How many squares are in this church window?

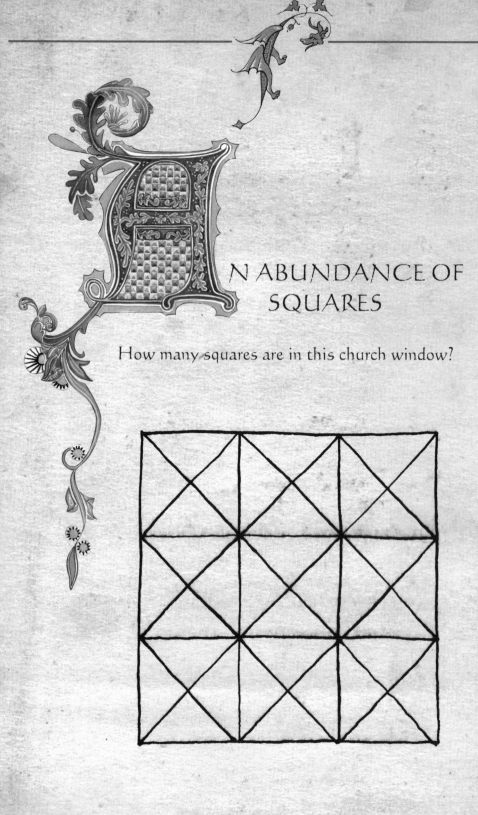

Solution p. 208

THREE GOBLETS

By turning two goblets at a time, the aim is to put them all the right way up in just three goes.

1   2   3

Now that you've managed this without any problem, I'm going to show you a secret so that you can challenge anyone who thinks it's easy ...

ARDBOARD

Today is Saint Louis' birthday. To mark the occasion, one of his courtiers gives him a lovely card which is 1 ft (30cm) long. The sovereign then announces to the assembled company: "I'm going to put my head through this card!"

The courtiers burst out laughing, but the king manages it…

How?

Solution p. 210

ALENDAR

If some months have 30 days and others 31, how many months have 28 days?

HREE SQUARES

An architect is studying the plans of a church he is building. He is using matches as an aid and wonders how he can get three squares by moving four matches.

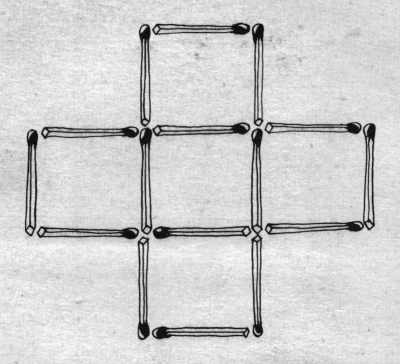

Solution p. 212

WHAT AM I?

You can keep me or share me.
But if you share me, I will disappear for ever.

What am I?

IRE IN THE DUNGEON

The fire alarm is raised in one of the castle's dungeons. To escape the flames and save his kingdom's crown jewels, the king, the queen and the crown prince borrow some rescue baskets which work as follows: if one basket is heavier than the other, it descends; a lever effect causes the other basket to rise and it comes to a stop in front of the escape window. But the load in the descending basket must never exceed that in the other basket by more than 15 kg; if it does, the speed of descent rises sharply and it becomes dangerous.

If the king weighs 95 kg,
the queen 55 kg,
the prince 40 kg and
the treasure 25 kg,
what must they do to escape the fire?

KING 95
QUEEN 55
PRINCE 40

TREASURE 25

Solution p. 214

 YSTERY

Draw three straight lines on this M to create nine triangles:

1

142 857

142 857 × 1 = 142 857   142 857 × 2 = 285 714
142 857 × 3 = 428 571   142 857 × 4 = 571 428
142 857 × 5 = 714 285   142 857 × 6 = 857 142

Why is the number 142,857 a magic number?

Solution p. 216

WHAT'S HAPPENED TO NORTH?

Try this curious experiment …

Make a compass by cutting an octagonal shape out of cardboard, and on each side draw an arrow pointing north. Rotate your compass while holding it in one hand between your thumb and index finger. Before and after this rotation, both 'needles' will point north. But this compass can go wrong … If you repeat the operation, one of the needles will indeed point north while the other will point south!

Rotate it again, and this time, one of the needles will still point north but the other will point east!
Try another rotation and you will see one needle pointing north, and the other west!

If you do one last rotation, everything will be back to normal; both needles will be pointing north …

Can you explain this strange phenomenon?

Solution p. 217

 **EVEN ROSEBUSHES AND SIX ROWS**

Sister Blanche is planting rosebushes in the gardens of Fontevrault Abbey. She has an eye for aesthetics, and means to create a harmonious flowerbed.

How should she arrange her seven rosebushes so that there are six rows, each containing three rosebushes?

Hint: a rosebush can belong to more than one row.

Solution p. 218

PHIALS

Three ladies of the court have sneaked into Merlin's laboratory and stolen 21 phials containing the elixir of youth. But they are somewhat disappointed to discover that while seven phials are full, seven are only half-full and seven are empty.

How should they go about sharing the secret of eternal life equally, so that each has the same number of phials and the same amount of elixir?

Note that the three ladies are unable to open the phials to check their contents.

NE STROKE OF THE PENCIL

Can you recreate this figure without lifting your pencil off the page and without going over the same line twice?

Solution p. 220

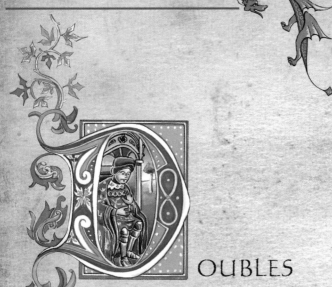

OUBLES

Which two of these blazons are identical?

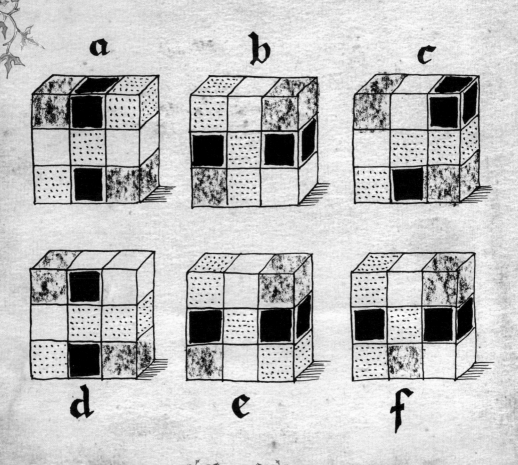

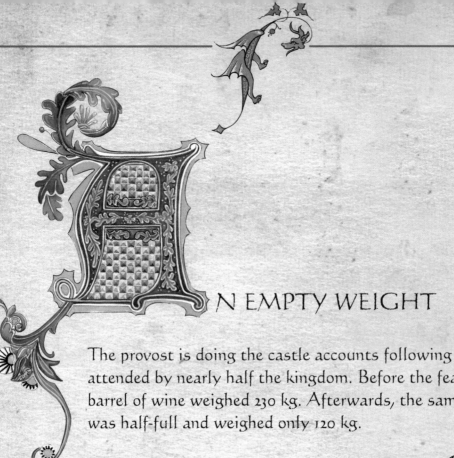

AN EMPTY WEIGHT

The provost is doing the castle accounts following a banquet attended by nearly half the kingdom. Before the feast, the barrel of wine weighed 230 kg. Afterwards, the same barrel was half-full and weighed only 120 kg.

What does the empty barrel weigh?

230

120

Solution p. 222

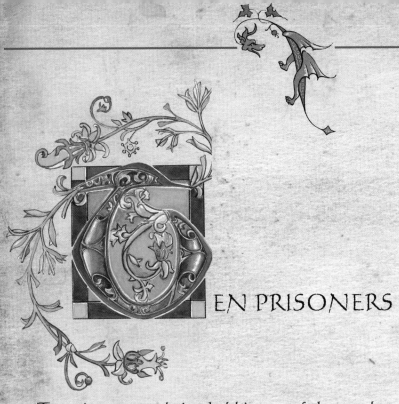

EN PRISONERS

Ten prisoners are being held in one of the royal castle's towers. To stop them from killing each other, the gaoler decides to separate them by erecting three circular cells.

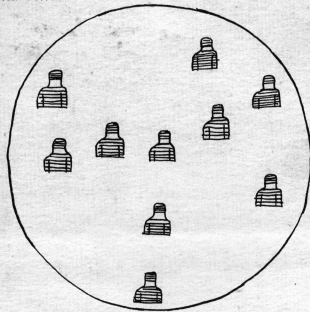

Where should he position them to isolate each prisoner?

BLACK IS BLACK (BEGINNER)

Shade in the white circles in such a way that the numbers in the boxes indicate how many black circles surround them.

Solution p. 224

 LACK IS BLACK
(ADVANCED)

Shade in the white circles in such a way that the numbers in the boxes indicate how many black circles surround them.

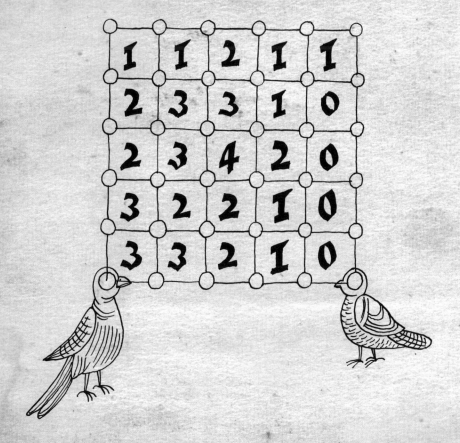

The grid contains the following numbers:

1	1	2	1	1
2	3	3	1	0
2	3	4	2	0
3	2	2	1	0
3	3	2	1	0

JUST RECTANGLES

How can the carpenter's apprentice down in Fishing Cat Lane make this figure contain only
rectangles, just by removing nine matches?

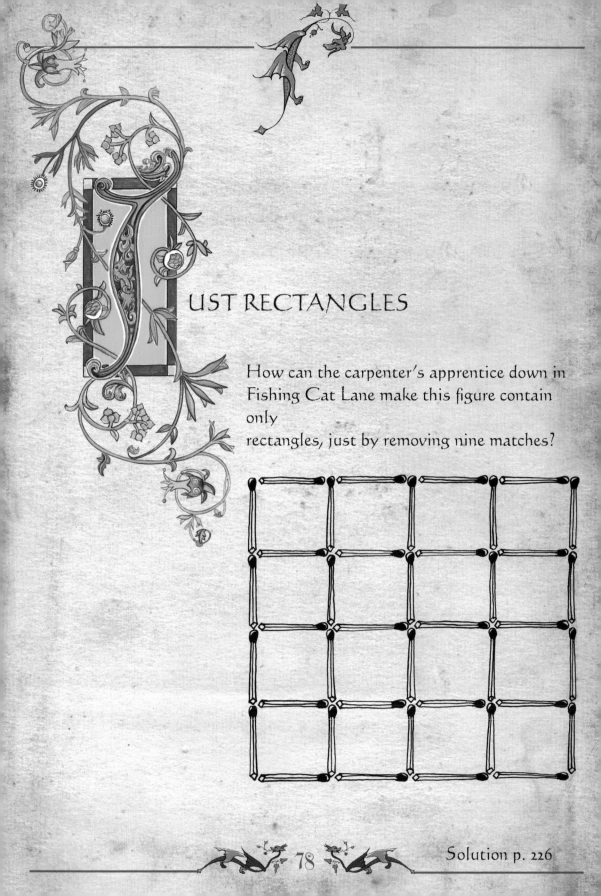

Solution p. 226

JUST SQUARES

And now, how can he get four identical squares by removing six matches?

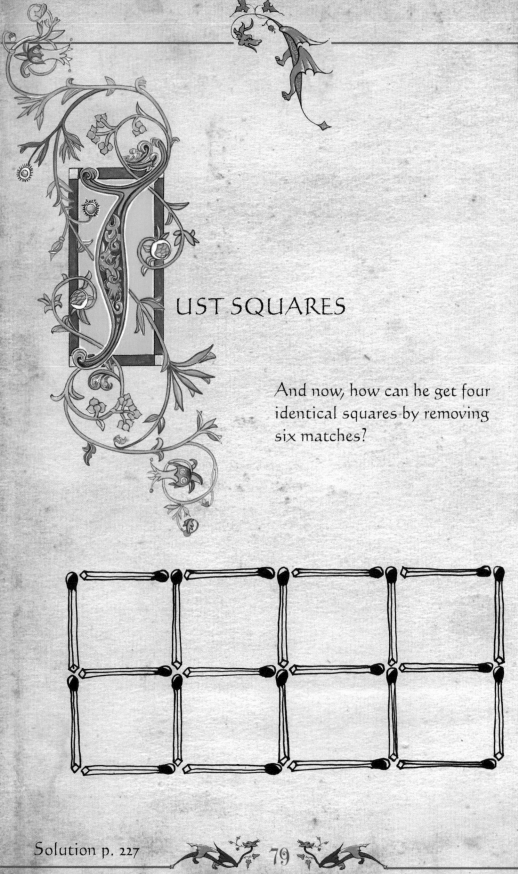

 **IX SQUARES**

Finally, how can our apprentice carpenter make six identical squares appear by adding eight matches?

Solution p. 228

TROLLS AND MEN

Everybody knows that trolls and humans do not get on. One day, three trolls and three humans had to cross a river by boat.

The trolls and the humans agreed to cross the river together, but with two conditions:

-- there must never be, on each crossing, more than two people on the boat;
-- trolls must never outnumber humans on the river bank at any time (ie whenever there is a changeover, a tally has to be kept of the number of individuals on the bank).

How should they set about it?

HOW DO YOU WEIGH A NUMBER?

If the weight of a number is equal to the sum of its figures, what is the smallest number that will weigh 25?

Solution p. 230

PENTAMIDOKU

This is a mixture of sudoku and pentamino (a sort of 5-squared domino).

The aim is to place the letters A, B, C, D and E in each pentamino in such a way that they never appear twice in any row or column.

THE NAKED EGG

How do you remove the shell from an egg without cooking it first?

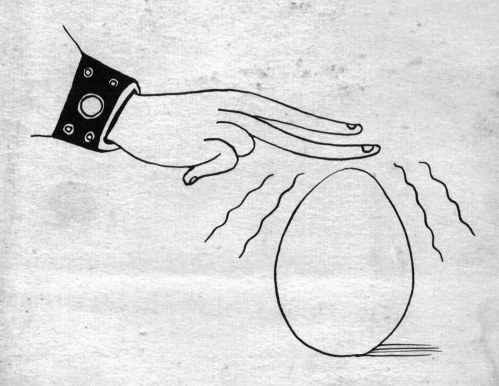

Solution p. 232

 HEERS!

On his return from the Battle of Soissons, Clovis has organised a victory feast for his knights. The festivities are in full swing and the mead is flowing freely. The provost, who occupies the apartments above the great hall, is trying to get some sleep but without success. When the convivial gathering decides to make a toast to victory, the provost hears the clinking of glasses thirty-six distinct times.

From this, can he work out how many guests are present that night?

WHERE ARE THE CUBES?

How many cubes must be added to this geometric figure to make one giant cube?

Solution p. 234

HE SOUND OF THE NUMBER

Here is a trick you can learn with a little practice. Get a box of matches and tell a friend to take some out -- it doesn't matter how many.

Then ask him to count how many matches are left in the box (but not to tell you), to add the two digits together and to remove that number of matches from the box. For example, if he has left 45 matches in the box he should take out 4 + 5, ie 9 matches.

So there are now 45 - 9, ie 36 matches left in the box, and there's no way you could know that ... And yet, you are going to take the box, shake it and confidently announce how many matches are still inside.

What is the secret?

IT DOESN'T GO ROUND!

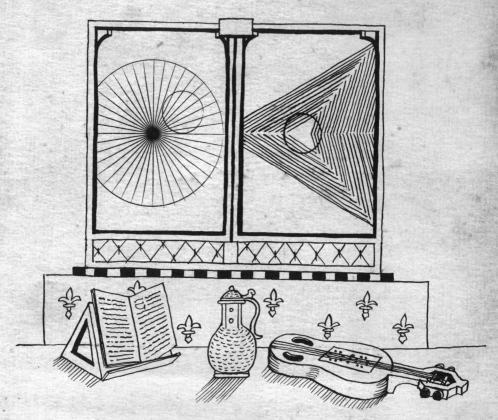

Standing in front of the windows of the castle's great hall, the provost thinks to himself:

"Those two circles there -- are they perfectly round?"

TWENTY QUESTIONS IN THE TAVERN

A spice merchant enters a tavern in Bordeaux and orders the chef's special, a cormorant stew.
As soon as the dish is served, the merchant takes a mouthful and immediately bursts into tears.

Why?

Riddles entitled "Twenty Questions" are more enjoyable if there are several of you. You ask the riddle and in order to solve it the audience asks you up to twenty questions to which you may only reply "yes" or "no"...

 UPERSTITION

Nostradamus made the following prediction: The year 2052 is destined
to be melancholy since it will begin on Friday the thirteenth!

So will you be celebrating that New Year's Eve?

Solution p. 238

HAINWORK

Lord Aubrey wants to make a chain necklace for Lady Margot from four separate pieces:

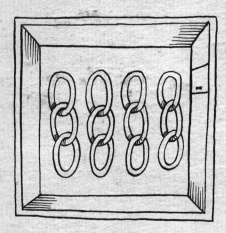

To break one link costs 5 farthings, and it costs 10 farthings to solder it together again.

What is the cheapest way to make a complete chain and how much will it cost Lord Aubrey?

ACKWARDS AND
FORWARDS

You are feeling rather lazy …

In the basement of your house are three switches, all currently off,
one of which will turn on the light in the attic.

From the basement you can't see the light in the attic, but you want
to be able to tell which is the right switch without having to go up
to the attic more than once.

How might you go about this?

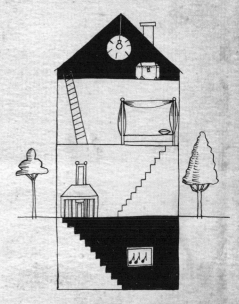

Solution p. 240

WHAT AM I?

I begin with an E.

I end with an E

I only contain one letter, but I am not the letter E.

 IVE TRIANGLES

Up in the cathedral bell-tower, a workman on his break wonders how he can make five triangles by moving five matches.

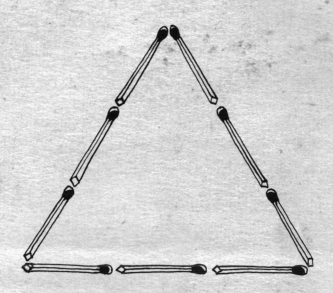

Solution p. 242

 OUR TRIANGLES

Now he has a go at making four identical triangles by moving five matches.

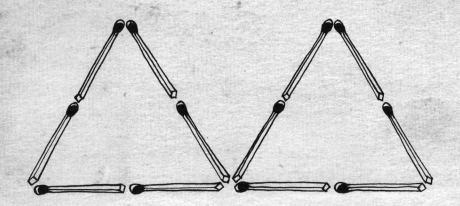

GLASS PYRAMID

During a feast at the castle, one of the waiting staff decides to issue a challenge for the amusement of the assembled company. He arranges three glasses so as to form a triangle:

Next he asks the guests to place a fourth glass on top of the others. To help them do this, he gives each person three knives which are shorter than the distance between the glasses. What should they do to take on the challenge and win?

Solution p. 244

TEN FINGERS MAKE NINE

Do you know your 9 times table?
1 × 9 = 9; 2 × 9 = 18; etc.

It might seem difficult to memorise, yet you only have to look at your hands and you'll never forget it!

How might that be?

ARSENIC

The queen has a plan to get rid of the king's mistress. Knowing that the mistress is unwell and that she has to take a pill every day, the queen calls on the services of one of those women who are skilled in making poisons, and hands over 12 boxes of her rival's pills to be replaced with arsenic.

But the old witch dies before she can accomplish her deadly mission, only having had time to substitute the pills in one of the 12 boxes.

The queen knows that the arsenic-laden pills weigh 1 g less than the harmless pills, which weigh 10 g.

There isn't much time ... how can she, with the help of some scales, find the box that has been tampered with?

Solution p. 246

HECK MATES

Thibaud and Clothaire play chess once a week. Last Monday they played five games and each won as many as the other, yet no game ended in a draw, nor was any game left unfinished.

How can this be?

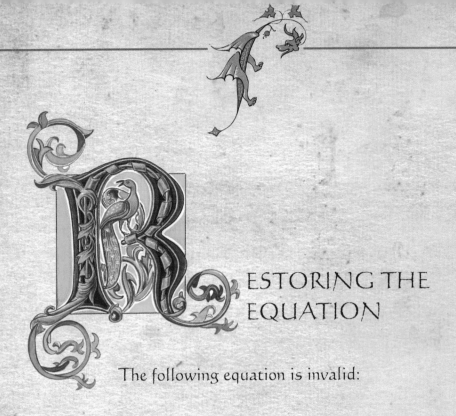

RESTORING THE EQUATION

The following equation is invalid:

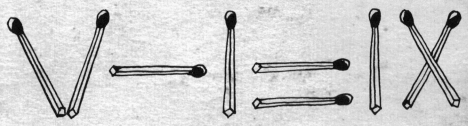

How can you make it valid just by moving one match?

Solution p. 248

THREE PILES

Here's a card trick you can learn with a bit of practice ...

Put the cards into three piles, face up, with nine cards in each. Ask a friend to look at all three piles and to make a mental note of one card, telling you only which pile the card is in.

Lay the cards out two more times, still making three piles, and ask them to tell you each time which pile their chosen card is in.

Now put all the cards together. Take the two top cards and put them on the table. Take the next two cards and put them at the bottom of the pack.

Take the next two cards and put these on the table. Keep doing this until there is only one card left in your hands: it will be your friend's card!

What is the secret?

Solution p. 249

ADAM AND EVE IN TWENTY QUESTIONS

During an expedition to the furthest icy reaches of Scandinavia, a Viking comes across two bodies, entombed in the ice in a perfectly preserved state.

After examining the bodies, he declares:

"These are the corpses of Adam and Eve!"

Why is he so sure?

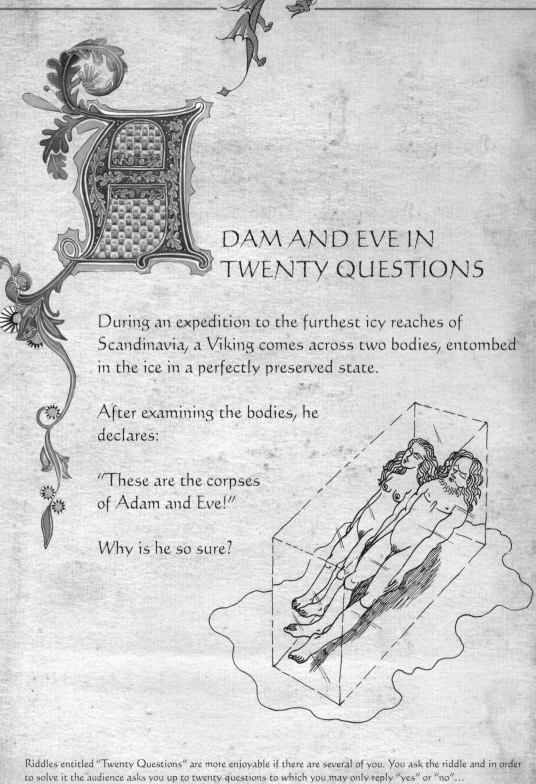

Riddles entitled "Twenty Questions" are more enjoyable if there are several of you. You ask the riddle and in order to solve it the audience asks you up to twenty questions to which you may only reply "yes" or "no"...

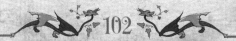

Solution p. 250

OTTERING ON THE TIGHTROPE

During a performance in honour of King Pépin the Short, a tightrope-walker crosses the castle courtyard on a narrow rope. To maintain his balance, he holds a pole with his hands about 31 inches (80 cm) apart, palms pointing upwards. When he reaches the end of the rope, a particularly scatterbrained assistant hands him another pole about 120 cm long, but fails to make sure it is centred in relation to his hands. One end of the pole is therefore perilously close to one of the acrobat's hands. He tries to recover his balance and moves his hands towards each other carefully and at the same speed.

Which way does the pole fall?

O END OF RECTANGLES

This diagram represents the paved floor of a castle's throne room. How many rectangles does it comprise?

Hint: a square is a type of rectangle …

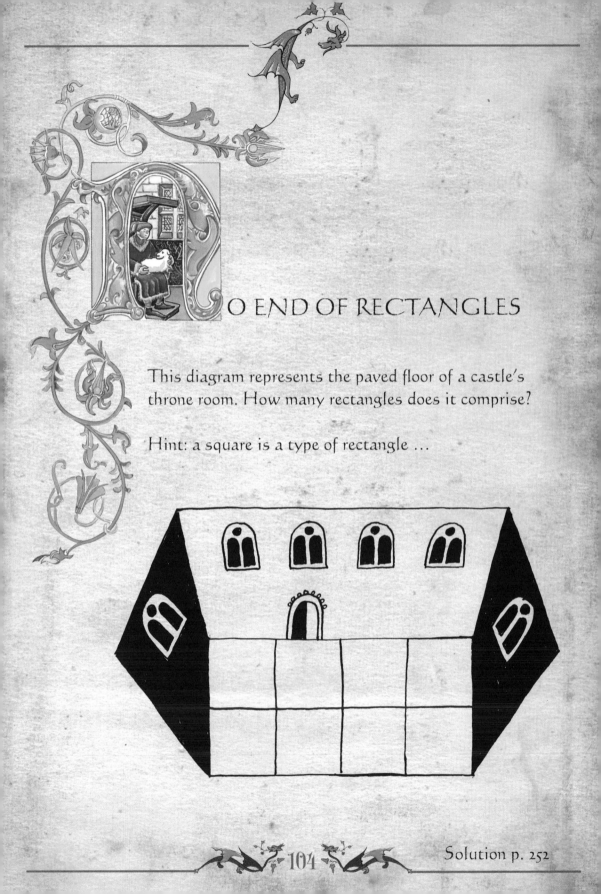

Solution p. 252

HE FIFTEEN DOORS

The provost has told Adhémar to lock all the castle doors for the night.

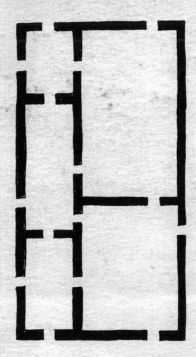

What route should he take to pass once and once only through each door?

NVELOPES

Place four sealed envelopes side-by-side.

Ask a friend to throw a die. Say it lands on a 2. Pick up the second envelope and ask your friend to check what is inside the other three. They will be empty.

Now give your friend the envelope that corresponds to the throw of the die and ask them to open it. Inside they will find a card on which is written:

"I knew you were going to choose this envelope."

How do you do it?

Solution p. 254

 OUNTING WITH LETTERS

Replace the letters with the numbers 1 to 9 so that this sum will work:

$$
\begin{array}{r}
a\,b \\
\times \quad c \\
\hline
d\,e \\
+\,f\,g \\
\hline
h\,i
\end{array}
$$

Note: each number can only be used once!

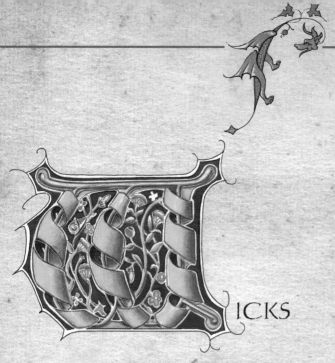

WICKS

Merlin has to let a potion rest for precisely 45 minutes, but he has nothing to measure the time with. On the other hand, he does have a torch and two wicks, which he knows will each burn for an hour but at an irregular rate (ie it won't take 30 minutes for half a wick to burn down).

How can the magician measure 45 minutes precisely?

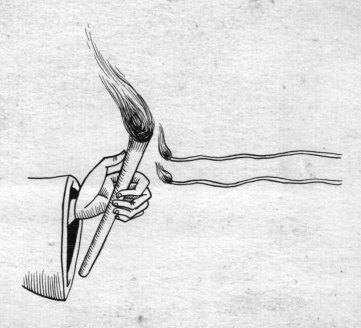

Solution p. 256

 IVE SQUARES

At the Fair, a troubadour has made this matchstick figure comprising five squares. How can he turn it into four identical squares just by moving four matches?

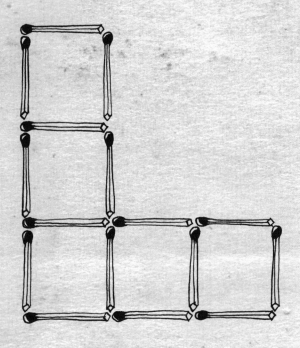

 IVE SQUARES PART 2

And now, how might he make four identical squares appear by moving just two matches?

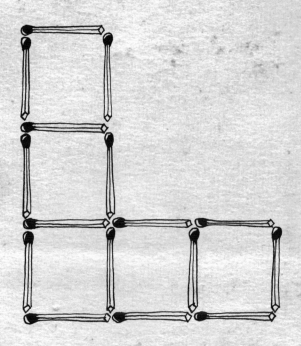

Solution p. 258

# BOUNCERS

If you drop a crystal glass, why does it only break on the last bounce?

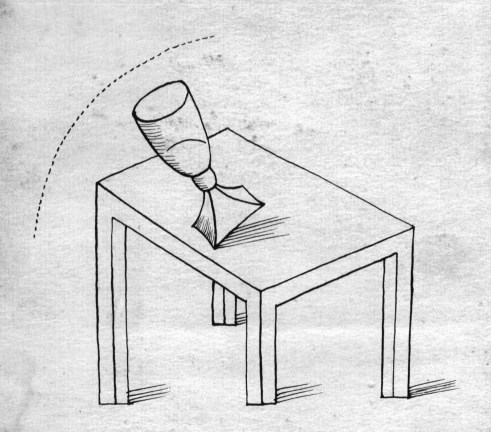

WO BOXES

You have three diamonds and two boxes which are different sizes.

Put the diamonds in the boxes in such a way that each box contains an odd number of diamonds.

Solution p. 260

 NE BOOK, ONE PAGE

How might you balance a book of spells on one single sheet of parchment?

 IVE CIRCLES

Substitute a number between 1 and 9 for each cross in such a way that the sum of the numbers in each of the five circles is the same.

Solution p. 262

EADS OR TAILS

King Clotaire III is bored … To amuse himself he lays out before him 12 coins as shown below:

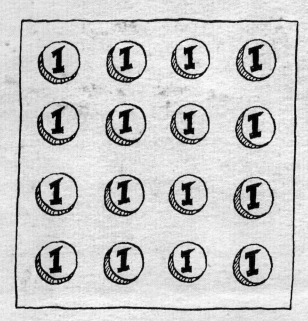

Which six coins must he turn over in order to leave an even number of coins with heads facing up each time they appear in a row or a column?

 OMBUSTION

Cut some cotton thread into two pieces, each about 1½ ft (45cm) long. Give one piece to a friend and ask them to tie a ring on one end. Then get them to apply a match to the thread: it will burn, and the ring will fall. So far, nothing unusual.

Now take the other piece of thread and do the same with a ring and a match, but this time you will see that the thread burns without breaking, and the ring doesn't drop!

What is the secret?

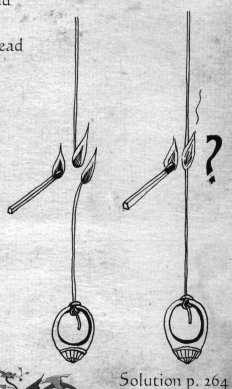

Solution p. 264

WET PAINT

If you had to number every side of this figure, how many sides would you end up numbering?

URDEROUS ROUTE

A prison is made up of 16 cells.

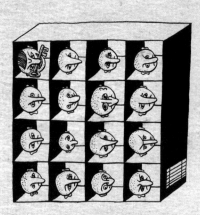

The prisoner in the top left cell has the key to the bottom right cell. Making up his mind to escape, he breaks down the wall of the neighbouring cell and murders the prisoner inside, leaving the body where it is. He continues like this through all the cells, murdering all the other prisoners, and never returns to a cell containing a corpse. Thus he manages to escape!

Can you work out his murderous route?

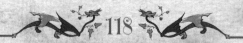

NUMBERS

Enter the numbers 0 to 9 in this multiplication sum in such a way that it works:

$$3$$

$$X \quad \blacksquare \; \blacksquare \; \blacksquare \; \blacksquare$$

$$\overline{}$$

$$\blacksquare \; \blacksquare \; \blacksquare \; \blacksquare \; \blacksquare$$

Note: each number can only be used once, and the 3 has already been entered.

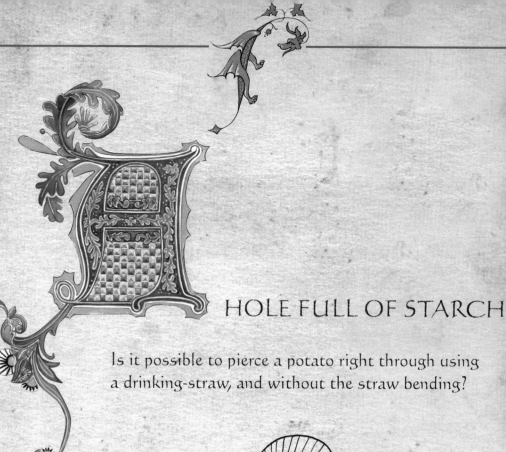

HOLE FULL OF STARCH

Is it possible to pierce a potato right through using a drinking-straw, and without the straw bending?

Solution p. 268

 ## INES AND COLUMNS

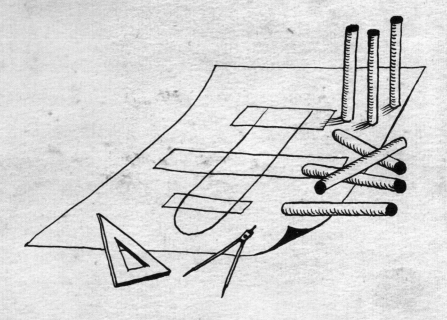

An architect is constructing a crypt beneath Chartres Cathedral. To support the structure, he knows he has to put up seven pillars. How should he set about positioning the seven pillars in such a way that he will get five lines each consisting of three pillars?

CRISTAN AND ISOLDE IN TWENTY QUESTIONS

Tristan and Isolde are lying dead in a pool of water on the floor of a castle chamber, surrounded by broken glass.

What happened?

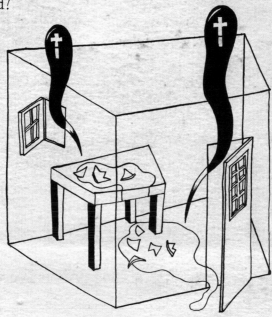

Riddles entitled "Twenty Questions" are more enjoyable if there are several of you. You ask the riddle and in order to solve it the audience asks you up to twenty questions to which you may only reply "yes" or "no"...

Solution p. 270

HREE QUEENS

In any order, place face up the queens of clubs, spades and hearts. I have my back to you and cannot see the cards.

I say to you: "Swap the queen of spades with the one to its right; if there is no card there, do nothing. Swap the queen of clubs with the one to its right; if there is no card there, do nothing. And finally, swap the queen of hearts with the one to its right; if there is no card there, do nothing. Now turn the cards over so that I can't see them."

At this point I turn round and I am able to announce confidently which card is in the middle ...

What's my secret?

Solution p. 271

VEHICLES

A bicycle moving at 60 mph overtakes a cart whose speed is a constant 45 mph.

For how long must the bicycle travel in order to be able to halt for five minutes without running the risk of being overtaken by the cart?

Solution p. 272

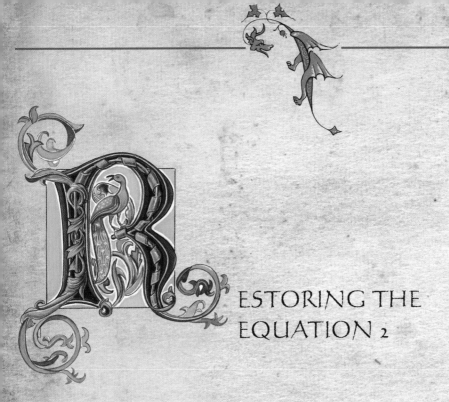

RESTORING THE EQUATION 2

The following equation is invalid:

How can you make it valid just by moving two matches?

 REEDOM

Thread a ring onto a cord and twist it once (figures A and B).

Take one end of the cord and thread it through the ring (figure C).

Ask a friend to take hold of both ends of the cord. Give the ring a pull: it will come off the cord (figure D).

Put the ring back into the original position and ask your friend to try to pull it off: they won't be able to free the ring ...

What is the secret?

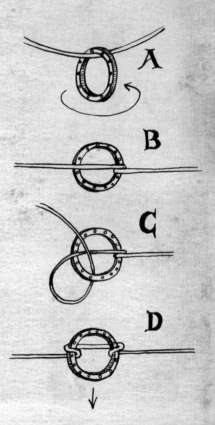

A

B

C

D

Solution p. 274

ALIMINATION

7	5	5	3	6	2
8	1	7	6	5	1
5	8	4	3	4	5
4	6	8	1	2	9
1	2	8	4	7	8
6	5	3	7	4	5

Remove 12 numbers leaving four numbers in each row and each column, so that each row and each column then adds up to 20 ...

ONFETTI

If you were to fold a sheet of paper in half, and fold it in half again four more times, and if you then snipped off the corners of the resulting rectangle, how many holes would there be when you unfolded the sheet of paper?

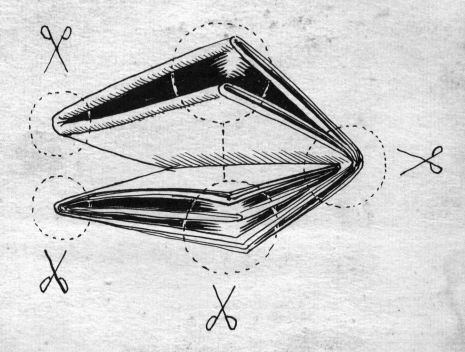

Solution p. 276

 OVE POTION

Merlin is preparing a love potion for King Arthur. According to his book of spells, he needs 4 fl oz of oil of toad. To measure the amount, he takes a flask filled with 8 fl oz of toad oil and two empty flasks, one with a capacity of 3 fl oz and one with a capacity of 5 fl oz.

With these, how is he going to be able to measure exactly 4 fl oz?

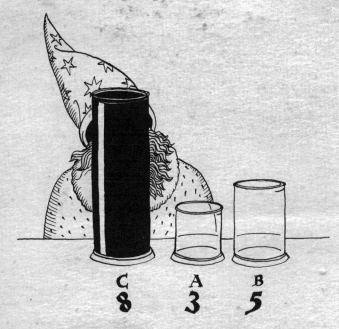

C
8

A
3

B
5

 NVERSION DIVERSION

Here are four cards representing four people:

How is it possible to turn all four cards upside down, while only turning three cards at a time a maximum of four times?

Solution p. 278

INN-SUFFICIENT SPACE

Twelve troubadours making their way to the Provins Fair, stop at an inn.

The innkeeper announces that despite only having 11 rooms available, he will be able to accommodate everybody.

He first takes two of the troubadours to Room 1 and asks them to wait until a room is free. He then puts the third person in Room 2, the fourth in Room 3, the fifth in Room 4, the sixth in Room 5 etc. The eleventh person he puts in Room 10. He goes back to Room 1 and asks one of the two troubadours to follow him to Room 11.

He has thus managed to accommodate 12 troubadours separately despite only having eleven rooms.

Or has he?

HE EARTH IS ROUND

The circumference of the Earth is around 40,000 km. Imagine you have a rope that long, which is tied around the Earth, assuming the surface is uniformly level. If the rope were hitched to one-metre-high poles all round the Earth, the circumference of the circle made by the rope would increase. How much extra rope would you need?

A   B

Solution p. 280

WHY MAKE FIVE WHEN YOU CAN MAKE NINE?

An alchemist is trying to make four additional squares appear by moving four matches. How should he go about it?

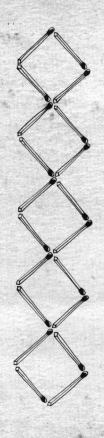

PUNCTURE-PROOF

A juggler challenges the crowd at the Feast of Saint John:

"I am going to use this knitting needle to pierce this balloon, and the balloon will neither burst nor deflate."

What is his secret?

Solution p. 282

EEDLE PIE

Try this strange experiment …

Take 100 needles, 2 ins long or thereabouts, and draw some parallel lines on the ground where the distance between them is twice the length of a needle.

Now drop the needles one by one quite indiscriminately over these parallel lines.

And now divide the total number of needles you have dropped by the number of needles that have landed across a line.

What do you get?

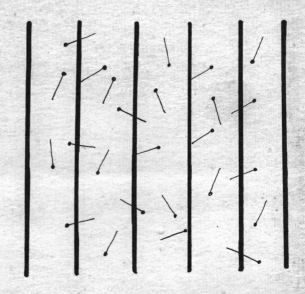

Solution p. 283

ANGLE OF A CUBE

What is a quick way to calculate the angle formed by the dotted lines on the sides of this cube?

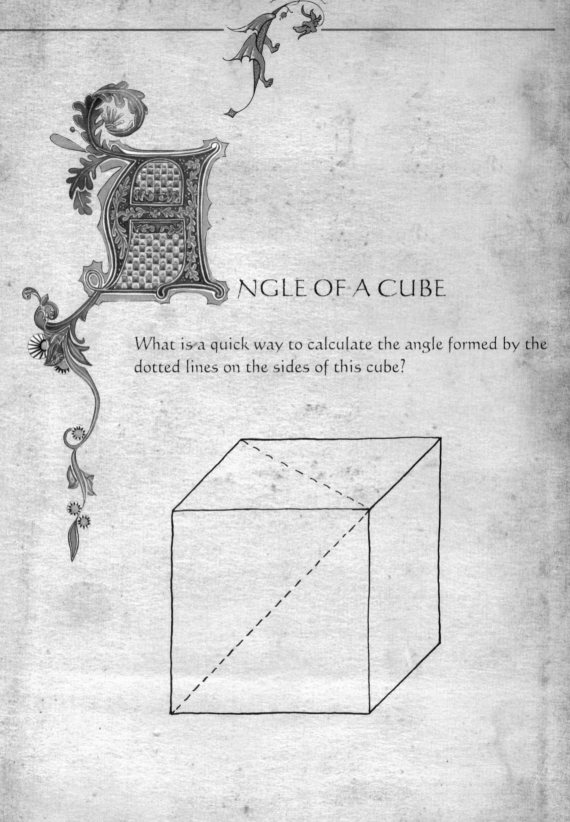

Solution p. 284

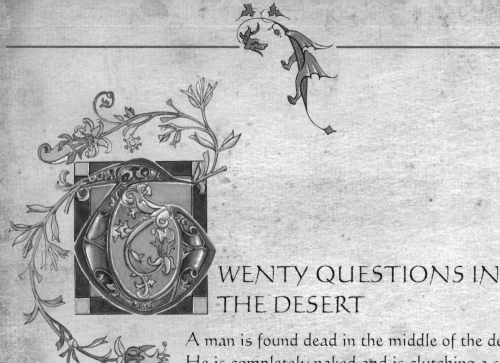

TWENTY QUESTIONS IN THE DESERT

A man is found dead in the middle of the desert. He is completely naked and is clutching a stalk of straw.

What happened?

Riddles entitled "Twenty Questions" are more enjoyable if there are several of you. You ask the riddle and in order to solve it the audience asks you up to twenty questions to which you may only reply "yes" or "no"…

Solution p. 285

HOW HARD DO WE REALLY WORK?

They say that a craftsman's work is difficult and exhausting, but is it really true?

Say the average working day is eight hours: that is one third of a whole day. The craftsman therefore works for a third of the year, ie 365 ÷ 3 or about 122 days.

But he rests on the last two days of each week, which amounts to 104 days a year.

If you take 104 from 122, that leaves only 18 full days of work.

And when you take into account time off for holidays and all the Bank Holidays as well, that adds up to more than 18 days throughout the year.

Conclusion: hard work isn't that hard!

This statement is patently false, but why?

Solution p. 286

ULLSEYE

At one stall at the Provins Fair, the audience is invited to try their luck at knife-throwing. If a participant manages to hit the target, he is given two more knives to throw.

Angus decides to have a go. If he had five knives when he started, and he has thrown seventeen knives in all, how many times did he manage to hit the target?

OOR TO DOOR

A man is imprisoned in a tower with two doors. Through one lies the way out and freedom, through the other - the ghastly dungeons. A guard stands in front of each door. One always tells the truth; the other always lies.

The prisoner just needs to ask one question, and to only one guard, to be certain of finding the route to freedom.

What is the question?

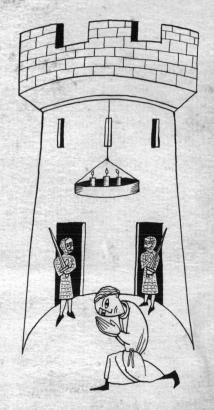

Solution p. 288

 ROM RECTANGLE TO SQUARE

A teacher asks his pupil to make six squares by moving three matches.

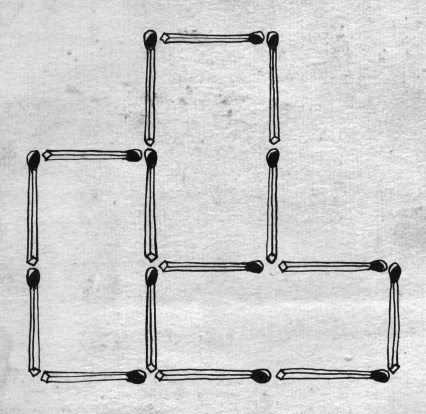

 ROM RECTANGLE TO SQUARE 2

He now asks his pupil to make three squares by moving three matches.

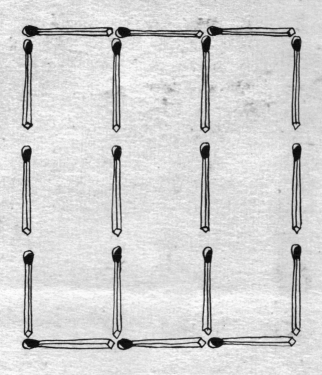

Solution p. 290

AMICABLE DIVORCE

Henry Plantagenet and Eleanor of Aquitaine are in love and have been married for 15 years. However, when Eleanor tells Henry she wants a divorce, Henry is delighted.

Why?

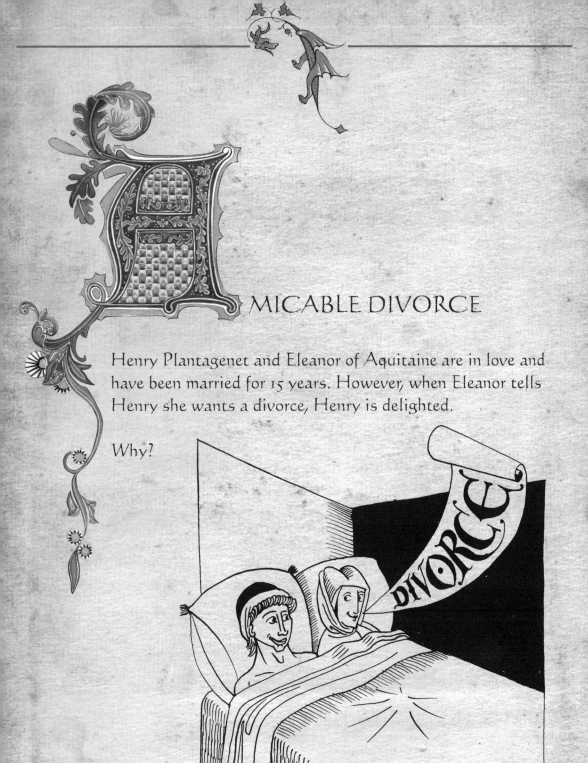

# IND THE NUMBER

Pick a number between 1 and 63, tell me which card or cards the number is on, and I will tell you the number you are thinking of.

A

1	3	5	7	9	11	13	15	17	19
21	23	25	27	29	31	33	35	37	39
41	43	45	47	49	51	53	55	57	59
61	63								

D

8	9	10	11	12	13	14	15	24	25
26	27	28	29	30	31	40	41	42	43
44	45	46	47	56	57	58	59	60	61
62	63								

B

2	3	6	7	10	11	14	15	18	19
22	23	26	27	30	31	34	35	38	39
42	43	46	47	50	51	54	55	58	59
62	63								

E

16	17	18	19	20	21	22	23	24	25
26	27	28	29	30	31	48	49	50	51
52	53	53	54	55	56	57	58	59	60
61	62	63							

C

4	5	6	7	12	13	14	15	20	21
22	23	28	29	30	31	36	37	38	39
44	45	46	47	52	53	54	55	60	61
62	63								

F

32	33	34	35	36	37	38	39	40	41
42	43	44	45	46	47	48	49	50	51
52	53	54	55	56	57	58	59	60	61
62	63								

What's my secret?

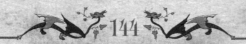

Solution p. 292

INESWEEPER

In this grid, certain cells are shaded.

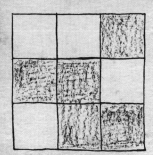

2	3	1
2	4	4
3	3	2

Here is a corresponding grid with numbers indicating, for each cell, how many of the surrounding cells should be shaded.

Can you work out which cells should be shaded if the numbered grid looks like this?

2	2	2
1	4	2
1	3	1

AX YOU CAN EAT

The provost of the chateau at Aix-la-Chapelle has produced a cake for Charlemagne's birthday.

When the cake is served, the King of the Franks blows out his candles and begins to tuck in. In keeping with his reputation for being a big eater, he wolfs down the whole cake and, still hungry, chews and swallows the birthday candles without batting an eyelid.

Could anyone really be that greedy?

Solution p. 294

 ARGE FAMILY

In the tavern are a father and a mother, a son and a daughter, a brother and a sister, a male cousin and a female cousin, and an uncle and an aunt. Each orders a flagon of mulled wine.

The landlord brings them a total of four drinks, yet each person gets one.

How is this possible?

T HE NAUGHTY MONK

Brother Stephen is in the scriptorium, paying
careful attention to a letter he is illustrating.
Unfortunately, Brother Gontran, who is sitting
next to him, is forever fooling around; he tries to distract Brother
Stephen from his task and keeps on flicking his ruler like this: he puts
the ruler on the edge of the table and gives a sharp tap to the end that
sticks out; the ruler literally flies up into the air before dropping back
to the ground.

A rather fed-up Brother Stephen
decides it's time to put an end
to these games and this
he achieves with the help
of just one sheet of the
parchment he's working on.

What does he do?

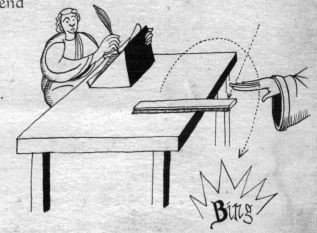

WASHERS

Fold a piece of string in half and thread the loop through the hole in a washer. Now thread the two ends of the string through this loop and tighten it so that the washer can't move. Lastly, thread four more washers over the loose ends of the string.

Ask two friends to hold one end of the string each without letting go, and announce:

"I am going to get the four washers off without cutting the string." You cover the whole thing with a napkin and put your hands beneath it. A few seconds later you will remove your hands and the four washers as well!

When the napkin is lifted, everyone will see that the original washer is still tightly in place.

What is the secret?

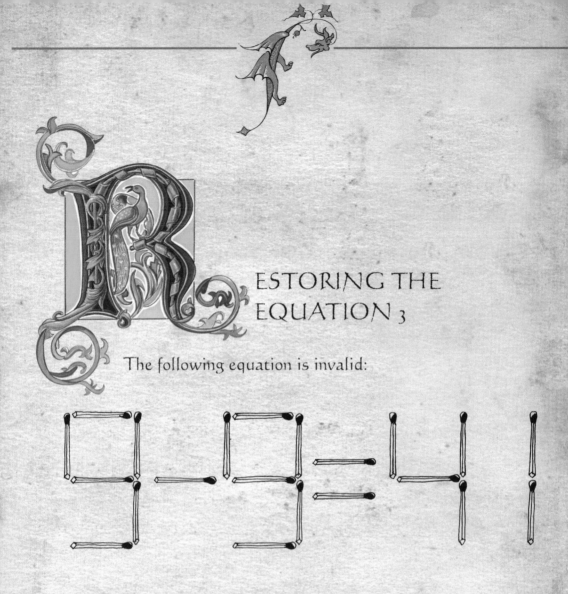

RESTORING THE EQUATION 3

The following equation is invalid:

How can you make it valid just by moving two matches?

Solution p. 298

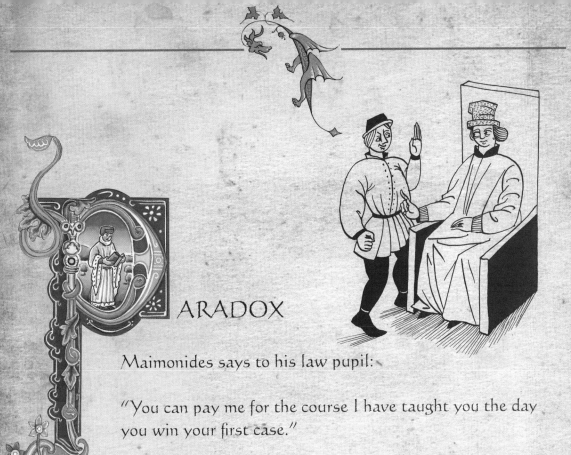

PARADOX

Maimonides says to his law pupil:

"You can pay me for the course I have taught you the day you win your first case."

But his pupil doesn't seem to be able to find any clients. An impatient Maimonides decides to go to court to recover his costs and issues a writ against his former pupil.
Once in court Maimonides announces:

"If I win this case, you will have to pay me in accordance with the decision of the court. If you win it, you will have to pay me according to the terms of our arrangement. Either way, I will be paid."

"Not at all!" retorts the pupil. "If I win, I won't have to pay you, in accordance with the decision of the court. If you win, I won't have to pay you according to the terms of our arrangement. So either way, I don't have to pay you."

Which of them has got it wrong?

 RUIT SALAD

As dinner comes to an end, Lord Sigismond tells his guest Fulbert that the knife he is holding has magic powers. He takes a banana from the fruit bowl and hands it to Fulbert to examine. It appears quite intact. Sigismond takes back the banana and makes as if to slice the fruit, but without ever actually touching it.

He again hands the banana to Fulbert and invites him to peel it. Fulbert is astonished to see that the banana has indeed been sliced!

Is Sigismonde's knife really enchanted?

Solution p. 300

TWENTY QUESTIONS IN THE FOREST

A man is found dead high up in a tree in the middle of the forest. He is wearing flippers, a mask and a snorkel.

What happened?

Riddles entitled "Twenty Questions" are more enjoyable if there are several of you. You ask the riddle and in order to solve it the audience asks you up to twenty questions to which you may only reply "yes "or "no"…

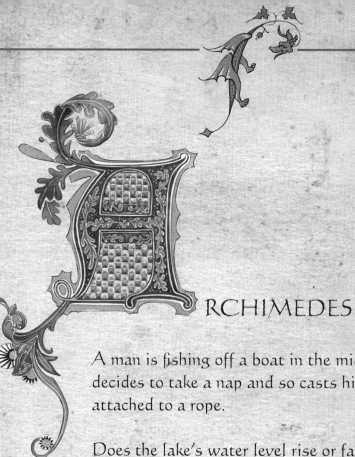

Archimedes

A man is fishing off a boat in the middle of a lake. He decides to take a nap and so casts his anchor over the side, attached to a rope.

Does the lake's water level rise or fall?

Solution p. 302

 ATE-KEEPER

Starting from any dot, draw a line to any adjacent dot (except diagonally) to create a closed figure whereby a number indicates how many walls of its cell are pencilled in.

Note: the last dot must join up with the first dot.

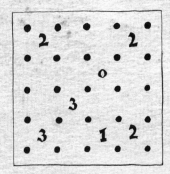 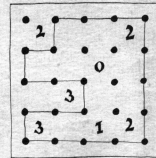

Can you now solve this one?

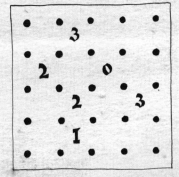

AIR TRADE

It is the Feast of Flowers, and Dame Cunégonde and Dame Hermance have brought food for the banquet which will bring the festivities to a close.

The former brings five dishes and the second, three.

Dame Ermangarde joins them, but she hasn't brought anything. The three friends share the food equally.

Dame Ermangarde suggests paying for her share by giving the other two 8 groats, which they then share out as follows: the one who brought five dishes receives five groats, and the other one, who brought three dishes, receives 3 groats.

But this calculation is not fair: why?

Solution p. 304

OLUTIONS

DIVINATION

In a 32-card deck, the 2s, 3s, 4s, 5s and 6s are missing.
We know that the number on the card is even: since it is not an
8, it must be a 10.
All that remains is to determine the suit: a black card that
isn't a club, must be a spade.

The card is therefore the 10 of spades.

Solution to p. 10

AGIC KNOT

All he has to do is cross his arms before taking hold of the ends of the rope. The juggler then uncrosses his arms, without letting go of the rope: a knot will miraculously form.

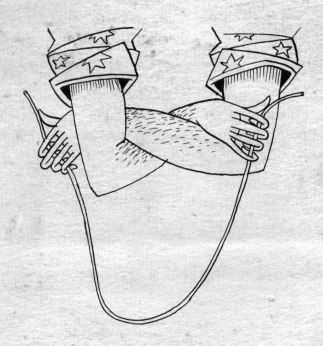

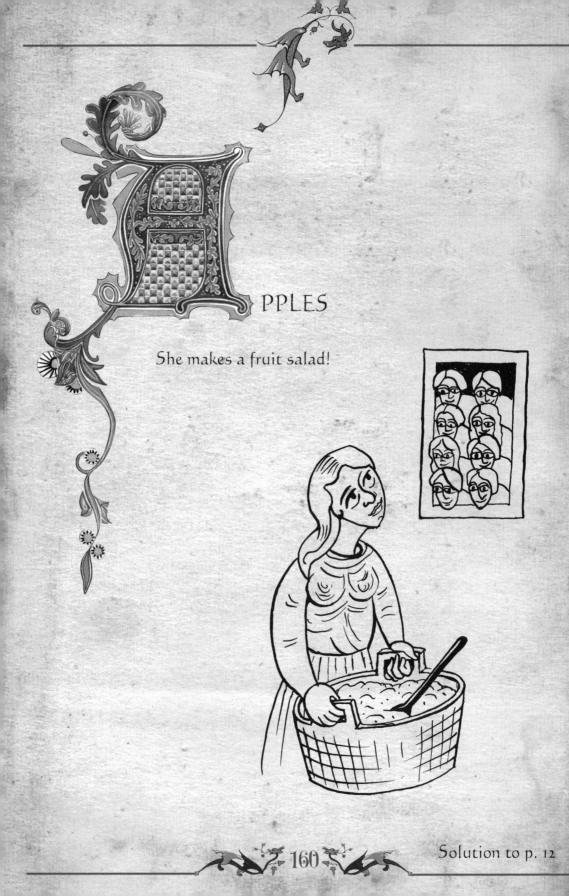

APPLES

She makes a fruit salad!

Solution to p. 12

YSTERIOUS PURCHASE

Godefroy de Bouillon is shopping for numbers for the front door of his castle. Individual numbers cost 3 groats each.

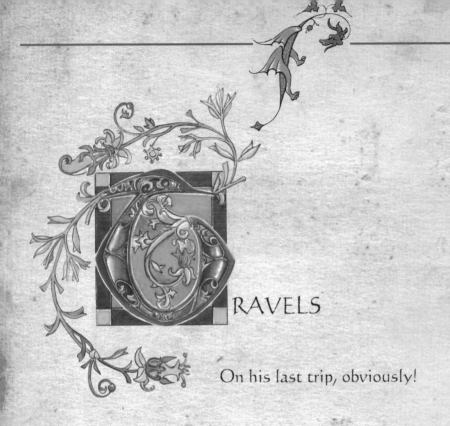

RAVELS

On his last trip, obviously!

Solution to p. 14

CROSSING OUT

The remaining numbers are:
1, 3, 4, 5, 7, 9, 11, 12, 13, 15, 16, 17, 19, 20, 21, 23, 25, 27, 28 and 29.

LLUSION

The two window frames are exactly the same height.

Odd, isn't it?

Solution to p. 16

 INE WINE

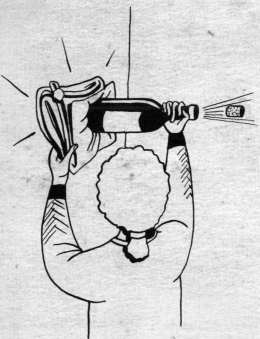

All he has to do is take the bottle by the neck and tap the bottom against a tree. After a few strikes, the cork will come out of the bottle of its own accord! He places his carefully folded cloak between the bottle and the tree to cushion it from the repeated blows.

SURPRISING SQUARE

Because the result contains all the numbers from 1 to 9, first in increasing and then in decreasing order!

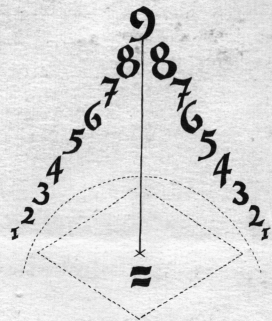

Solution to p. 18

P THE GREAT LADDER

The ladder has twenty-three rungs.
Here is a diagram of the workman's climb:

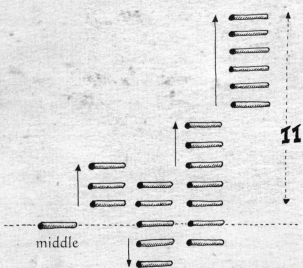

middle

11

Remember that at the beginning, the workman is on the middle rung:
the ladder must therefore have an odd number of rungs.

RIGAMI

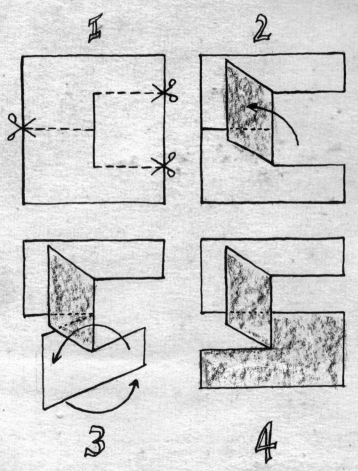

Solution to p. 20

HAT AM I?

I am a clock!

ABYRINTH

Solution to p. 22

TANDARD

 IGH TIDE

There will still be seventeen rungs: the boat floats, so the ladder rises at the same time ...

Solution to p. 24

PYRAMID OF ODD NUMBERS

The sum of the numbers on each line of this pyramid is equal to the cube of whatever line they are on:

1st line	$\rightarrow$	$1^3 =$	1
2nd line	$\rightarrow$	$2^3 =$	8
3rd line	$\rightarrow$	$3^3 =$	27
4th line	$\rightarrow$	$4^3 =$	64
5th line	$\rightarrow$	$5^3 =$	125
15th line	$\rightarrow$	$15^3 =$	3375

15th line

WINTER GARDEN

Baudouin is not surprised because his garden is twice as big as Gaël's!

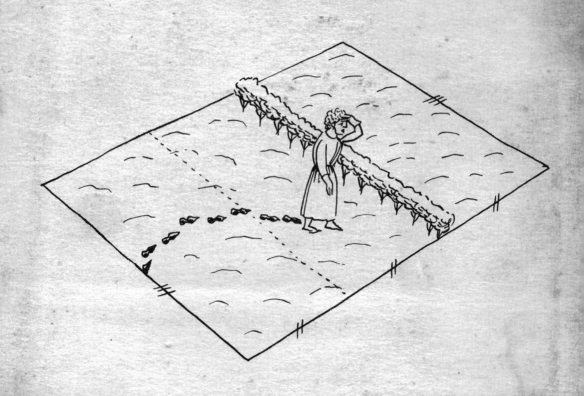

Solution to p. 26

WHAT AM I?

I am a second!
Since 1967, a second has been defined not in relation to a year,
but in relation to a property of matter.

 IGNS FOR A HUNDRED

$$1 + 2 + 3 + 4 + 5 + 6 + 7 + (8 \times 9) = 100$$

Solution to p. 28

 IGNS WITH FIVE

Here is one possible solution:

$$(5 \times 5 \times 5) - (5 \times 5) = 100$$

 ITORI

Solution to p. 30

OUR QUEENS

C1, D5, H2, K4.

	a	b	c	d	e	f	g	h	i	j	k	l
1			♛									
2								♛				
3												
4											♛	
5			♛									

PRISONERS

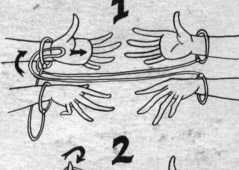

1

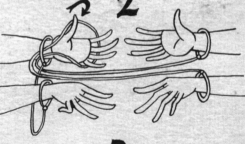

2

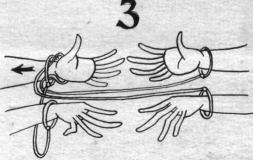

3

Free at last!

Solution to p. 32

 REEDY WHIM

Dame Berthe gives six biscuits to six children and hands the tin, in which she has left the last biscuit, to the seventh.

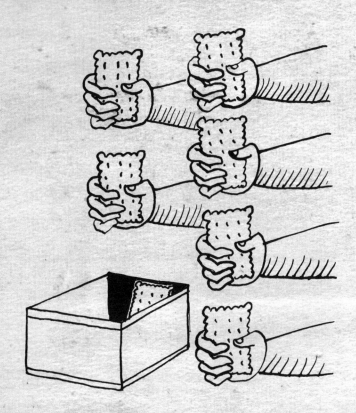

Solution to p. 33

 IX TRIANGLES

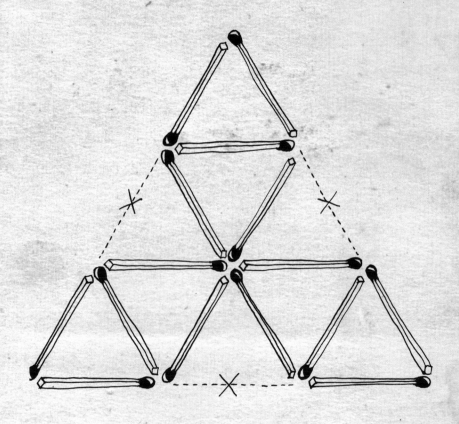

Solution to p. 34

 OUR TRIANGLES

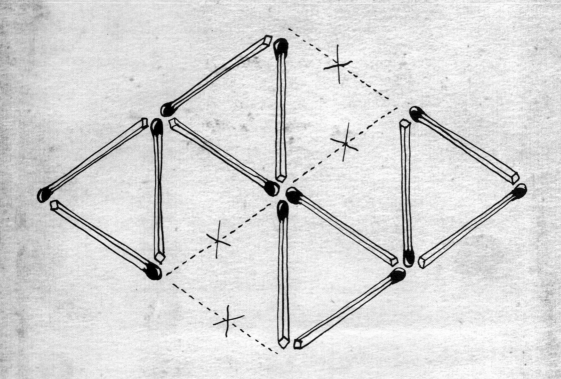

# SEVENTEEN STICKS

In order to win, Yvain has to make sure he picks up the sixteenth stick, which will force Galahad to take the last one. To achieve this he lets his opponent start, and however many sticks Galahad picks up, Yvain picks up as many as it takes to add up to four:

– if Galahad takes one stick, Yvain takes three;
– if Galahad takes two, Yvain takes two;
-- and if Galahad takes three, Yvain takes one.

In this way Yvain will take the fourth stick, the eighth, the twelfth and the all-important sixteenth stick which will allow him to win the game and so the heart of his lady.

Solution to p. 36

TROUBADOURS

Martin and Éberulf play all three instruments, and Léandre doesn't play any of them.

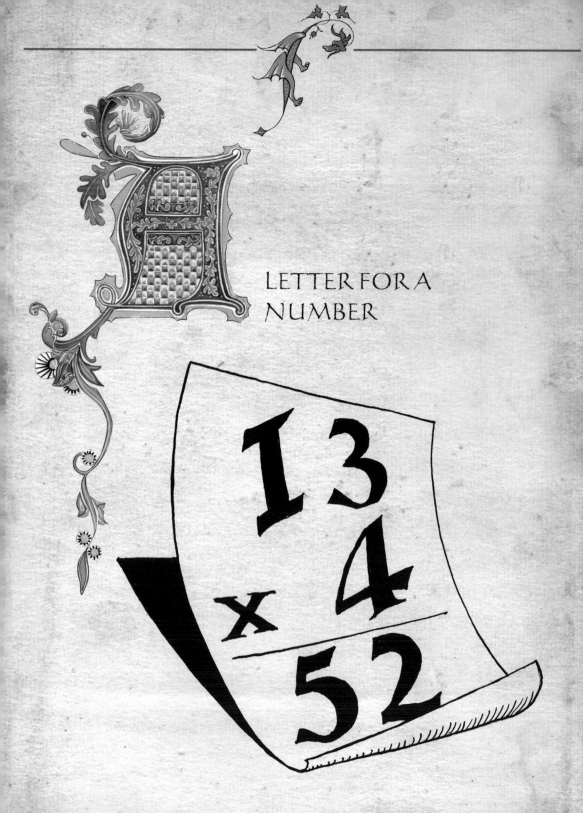

LETTER FOR A NUMBER

Solution to p. 38

 HAT AM I?

A coffin!

 N EQUAL PARTS

Simple!

Solution to p. 40

ARD CONUNDRUM

Solution to p. 41

 UNNY RULE

To understand this rule, we have to think in Roman numerals:

9   11   12   13

IX   XI   XII   XIII

In the literal sense, half of these numbers is therefore:

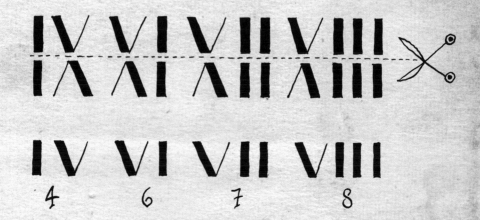

IV   VI   VII   VIII
4   6   7   8

Half of 13 (XIII) is accordingly 8 (VIII).

Solution to p. 42

URNING COINS

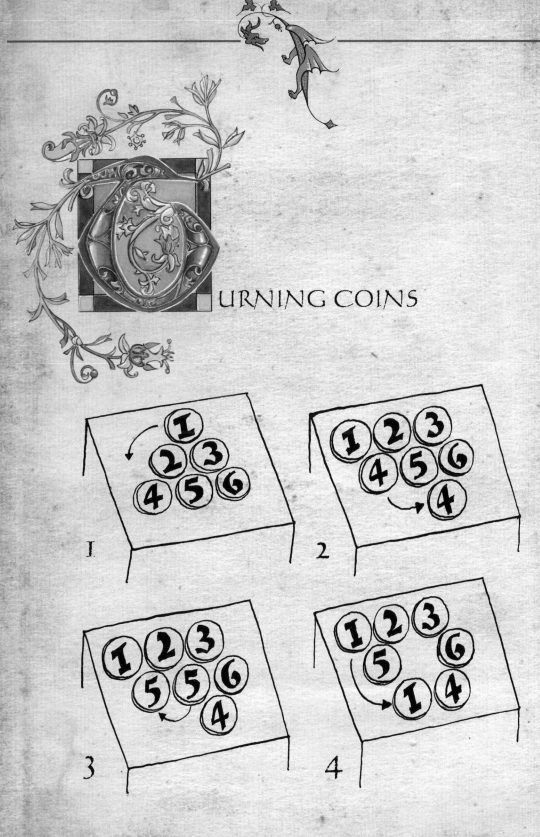

I.

2

3

4

HICKENS

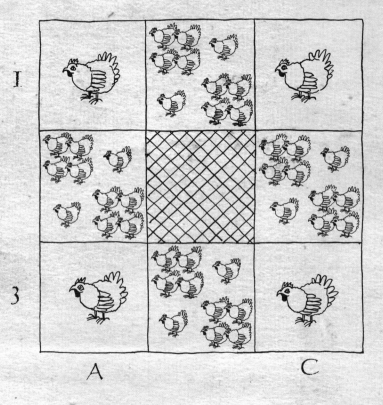

And there are your 44 chickens!

Solution to p. 44

OUNTAIN

Even before it was discovered, Everest was the highest mountain in the world!

PAYMENT

Childebert must give Sigismond 500 groats. Childebert will thus have 500 groats less, while Sigismond will have 500 groats more. Sigismond will therefore end up with 1,000 groats more than Childebert.

500

Solution to p. 46

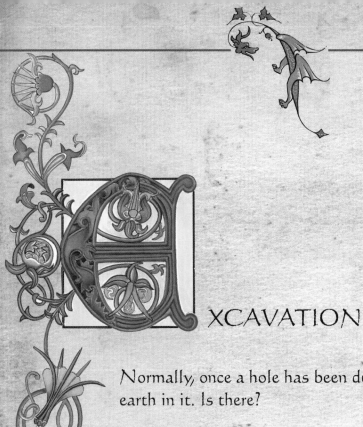

EXCAVATION

Normally, once a hole has been dug there isn't any more earth in it. Is there?

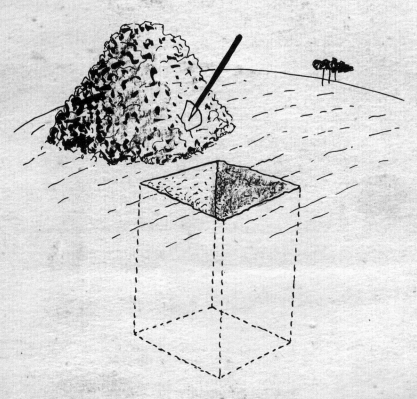

AGIC FIGURE

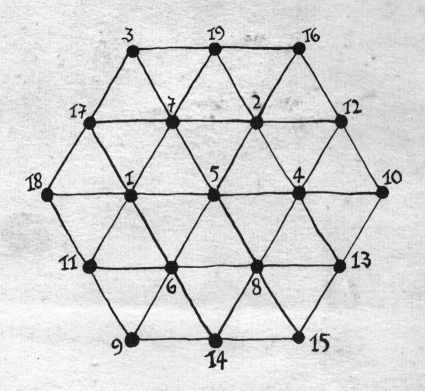

Solution to p. 48

ENEALOGY

Liébault is Landéric's grandfather.

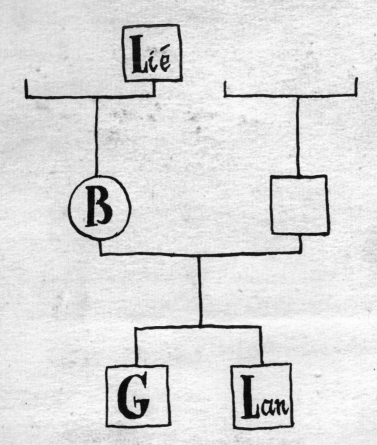

ONNECTIONS

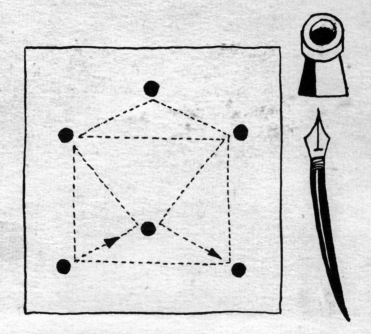

Solution to p. 50

RUEL DILEMMA

He has a chance if he opts to be thrown into the lions' pit. If they haven't eaten for five months, they have probably died of hunger!

AN UNLUCKY FARMER

The ones that are left are the survivors, so seven cows!

RAINS

Manhole covers are round so that they cannot fall into the hole they are covering! If the cover were square, it could slip through the hole diagonally.

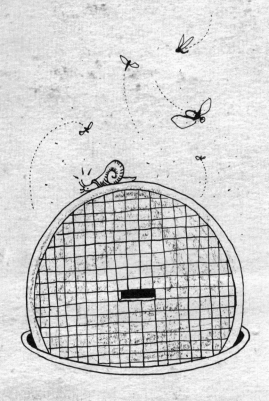

OLDS

This would not be possible unless the parchment were at least two and a half metres (over eight feet) wide!

If you try to fold an ordinary A4 sheet, you will find that you can't do it more than ... seven times!

Solution to p. 54

ORE FOLDS

After the first fold, we would have 2 layers on top of each other, ie 2 X 0.10 mm = 0.20 mm.

After the second we would have 4 layers on top of each other, ie 4 X 0.10 mm = 0.40 mm.

After the third, we would have 8 layers on top of each other, ie 8 X 0.10 mm = 0.80 mm.

After the fourth, we would have 16 layers on top of each other, ie 16 X 0.10 mm = 1.60 mm.

After the fifth, we would have 32 layers on top of each other, ie 32 X 0.10 mm = 3.20 mm.

...

By the time of the twentieth fold, we would have 1,048,576 layers on top of each other, ie 1,048,576 X 0.10 mm = 104,857.6 mm (or 104.857 m).

If we carried on folding, the parchment would, at the sixtieth fold, be 115,292,150,460 km thick!

Solution to p. 55

RAKING LEAVES

Just one, of course!

Solution to p. 56

IVISIONS

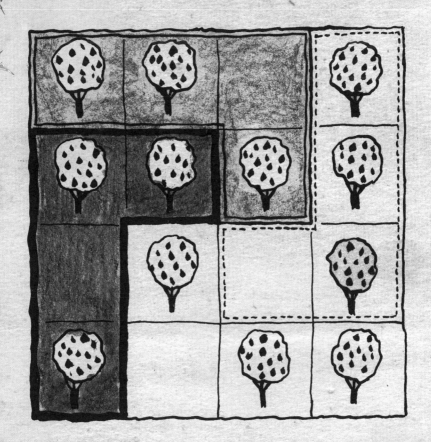

OMPULSIVE LIAR

Dame Frénégonde is telling the truth: she's talking about her father's mother, not her mother's mother!

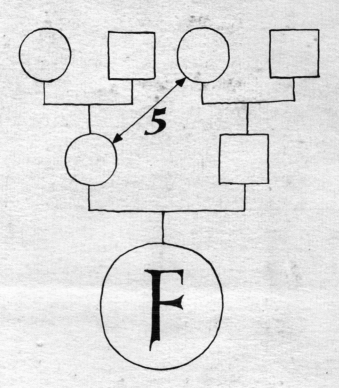

Solution to p. 58

THE COLUMN OF NUMBERS

The sum of the figures in the column is always the product of the sixth number multiplied by 11. For example, if the monk says the sixth number is 41, the Prior will reply 451, and this will turn out to be the total of the numbers.

Solution to p. 59

AN ABUNDANCE OF SQUARES

The window contains 31 squares: 1 square with 3 segments on each side, 4 with 2 segments on each side, 9 with 1 on each side, and 1 + 4 + 9 gives us 17.

Now if you tip your head 45 degrees to one side, you can see 17 more squares: 12 small squares like this:

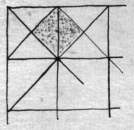

5 large squares like this (don't forget the one in the middle):

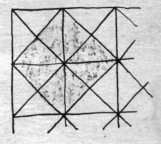

So the total is 14 + 17, ie 31 squares.

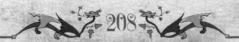
Solution to p. 60

THREE GOBLETS

By turning two goblets at a time, the aim is to put them all the right way up in just three goes.

After the challenge, the goblets are in this position:

Turn over the middle goblet and say " Your turn! "

It is now impossible to turn the goblets the right way up by moving two at a time, however many attempts …

Solution to p. 61

 ARDBOARD MAGIC

All he has to do is cut lines in the card as shown in the diagram below:

The result is a paper necklace which he can put round his neck!

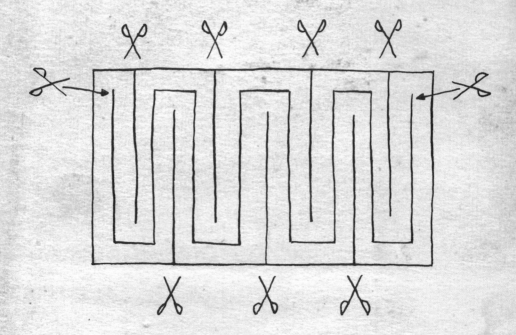

Solution to p. 62

 ALENDAR

All twelve of them, since they all have at least twenty-eight days!

THREE SQUARES

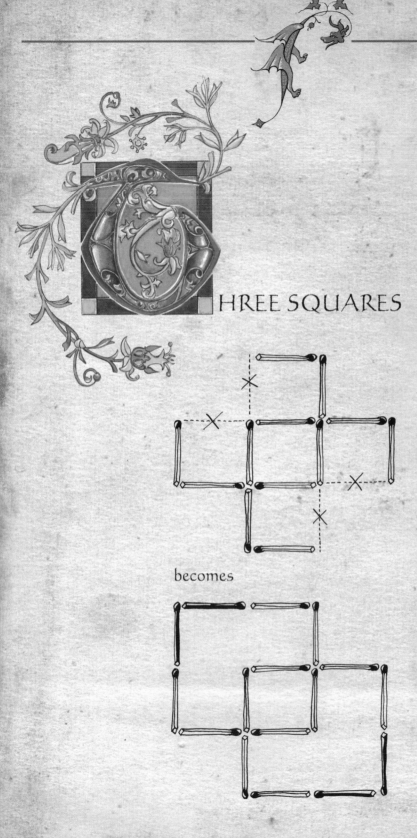

becomes

Solution to p. 64

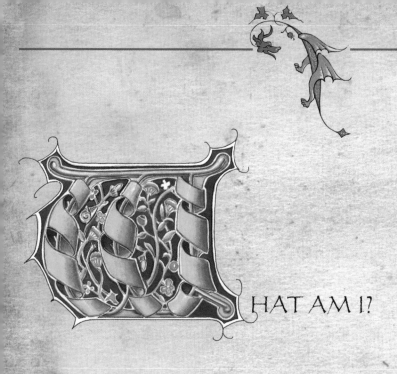

WHAT AM I?

A SECRET

Solution to p. 65

 IRE IN THE DUNGEON

1. First they put the treasure in one basket which goes down.
2. The prince then gets into the empty basket which slowly descends while the basket containing the treasure, which is lighter, climbs back up.
3. The queen exchanges places with the treasure and descends while the prince comes up again.
4. With the queen down below, the king puts the treasure into the basket which has just come up, and lets it drop.
5. The king can now gently descend while the queen and the treasure come up again in the other basket.
6. The queen once again lets the treasure drop.
7. The prince can now descend while the treasure goes up as a counterweight.
8. The queen exchanges place with the treasure while the prince is in the other basket going up.
9. The prince lets the treasure drop.
10. The prince can now come down while the treasure goes back up.
11. The king, queen and crown prince are safe.

All that remains is the treasure which has just dropped down to earth.

Solution to p. 66

 YSTERY

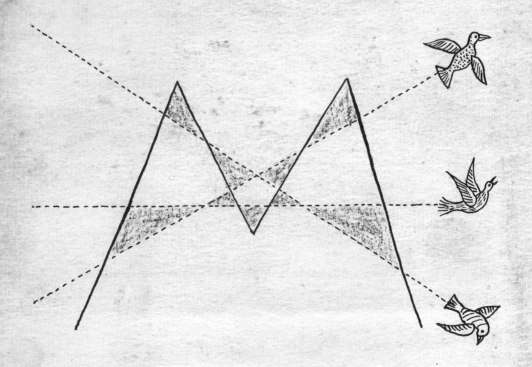

1

42 857

Here are the products of 142,587 when multiplied by 1, 2, 3, 4, 5 and 6:

ABC	DEF	
142	857	1
285	714	2
428	571	3
571	428	4
714	285	5
857	142	6

If you look a little more closely at the results, you will see that:
-- they are all made up of the six numbers comprising 142,857, and in the same order; only the starting number changes;
-- the sum of the numbers in each column is equal to the sum of the numbers in each row, ie 27;
-- if you add the first three numbers in each row to the second three, the answer is always the same: 999. 142 + 957 = 999; 285 + 714 = 999; etc.

So 142,857 really is a magic number!

Solution to p. 68

HAT'S HAPPENED TO NORTH?

This is a trick. You draw identical arrows on each side of your octagon, one pointing north on one side, the other pointing west.

The way you hold the compass is what creates the illusion that the 'needle' is moving.

The letters I and T indicate where you have to place your Index finger and your Thumb to make the trick work.

Hold the compass between the two fingers, either in the left or the right hand. Then make the compass rotate between the thumb and index finger using the other hand, to reveal one or other side.

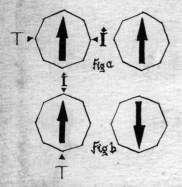

Figure A : both needles point north.

Figure B : one needle points north, the other south.

Figure C : one needle points north, the other east.

Figure D : one needle points north, the other west.

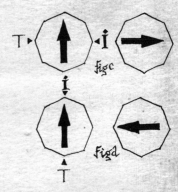

SEVEN ROSEBUSHES AND SIX ROWS

Here is one possible solution:

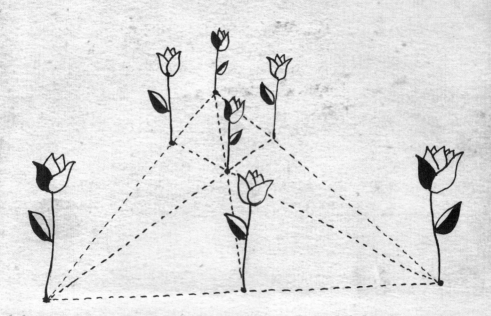

Solution to p. 70

HIALS

Here is one possibility:
-- the first lady takes three full phials, three empty ones and one which is half-full;
-- the second lady takes three full phials, three empty ones and one which is half-full;
-- the third takes one full phial, one empty one and five that are half-full.

NE STROKE OF THE PEN

Here is one possible solution:

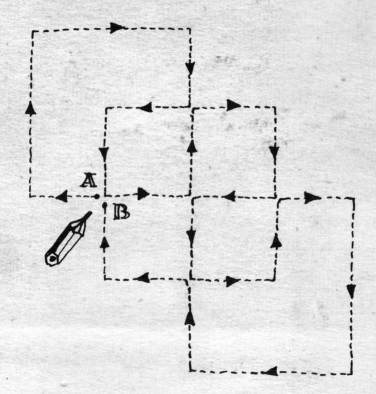

Solution to p. 72

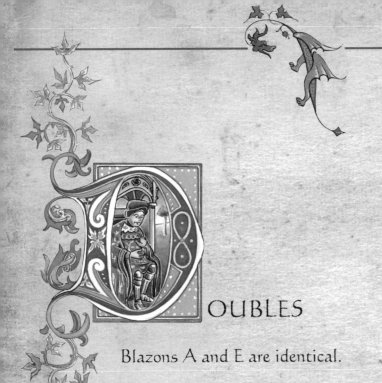

Doubles

Blazons A and E are identical.

A and E

AN EMPTY WEIGHT

The barrel weighs 10 kg.

The difference between the full barrel (230 kg) and the half-full barrel (120 kg) is 110 kg, ie the weight of the wine in the half-full barrel. The weight of the wine in a full barrel is therefore 110 X 2 = 220 kg.

The weight of the barrel is therefore 230 - 220 = 10 kg.

230   120   230-120
= 110

110x2   10
=220

Solution to p. 74

TEN PRISONERS

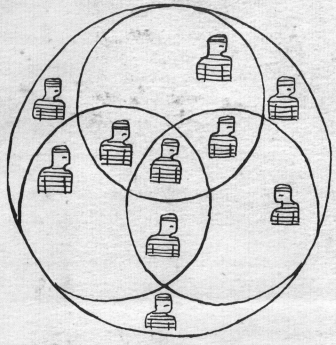

BLACK IS BLACK
(BEGINNER)

Solution to p. 76

BLACK IS BLACK
(ADVANCED)

JUST RECTANGLES

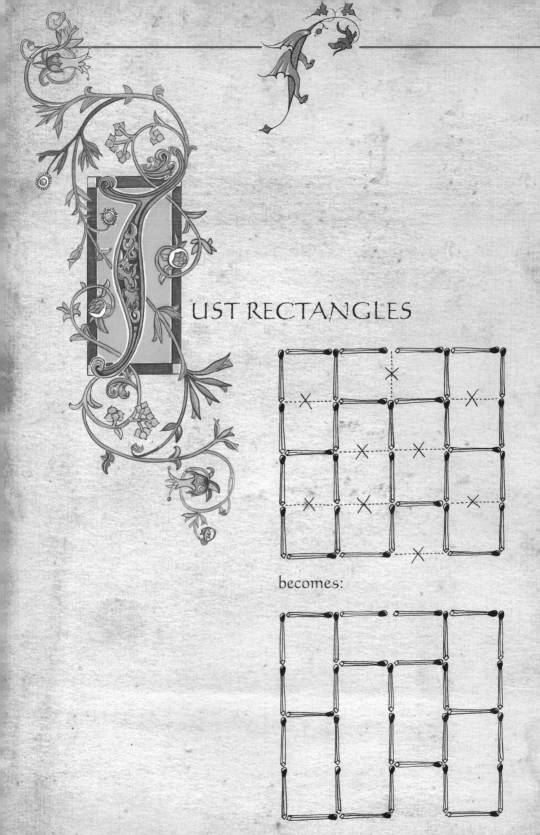

becomes:

Solution to p. 78

JUST SQUARES

becomes:

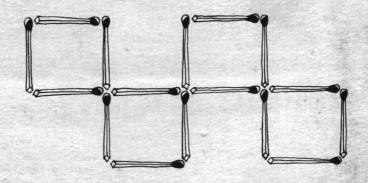

IX SQUARES

You just have to think in three dimensions.

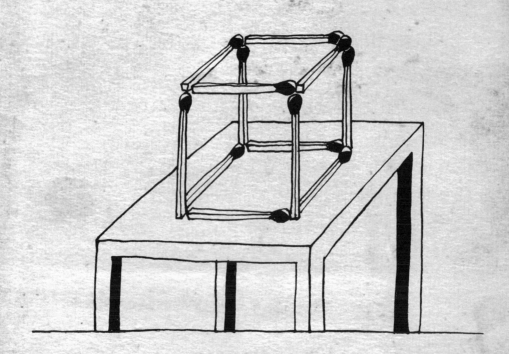

Solution to p. 80

TROLLS AND MEN

T = Trolls
H = Humans

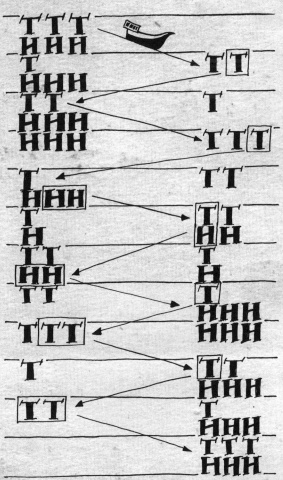

# HOW DO YOU WEIGH A NUMBER?

The answer is 799.

We need to find the number with the least figures.
If we divide 25 by 9, we can determine how many 9s are in the number we're looking for.
The remainder gives us the last figure in this number. As it is less than 9, it goes first.

Solution to p. 82

ᴘ ENTAMIDOKU

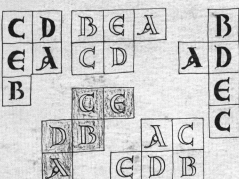

which gives us:

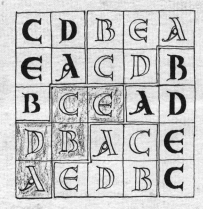

HE NAKED EGG

All you have to do is immerse it in white vinegar:
after some hours, the shell will have dissolved completely.

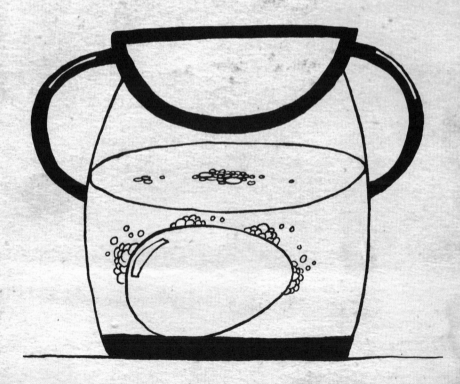

Solution to p. 84

CHEERS!

There are nine guests!
One guest will clink glasses with eight others, but the next will clink
with only seven others, and so on.

$8 + 7 + 6 + 5 + 4 + 3 + 2 + 1 = 36$ clinks, making nine guests.

WHERE ARE THE CUBES?

A B C D E

In section A, 2 cubes are missing.
In section B, 9 cubes are missing.
In section C, 10 cubes are missing.
In section D, 7 cubes are missing.
In section E, 3 cubes are missing.

Altogether 2 + 9 + 10 + 7 + 3 = 31 cubes must be added.

Solution to p. 86

THE SOUND OF THE NUMBER

The total number of matches left in
the box must be a multiple of 9!
So there will be 9, 18, 27, 36, 45, 54, 63 or 72 matches left.
When you shake the box, you will be able to tell how many matches
are inside just from the sound: the more considerable the noise, the
more matches are in the box.
The difference in sound between 18 and 72 is more marked than that
between 27 and 36, but with a little practice you will learn to distin-
guish between the two …

 T DOESN'T GO ROUND!

Yes, the circles are perfectly round.
Odd, isn't it?

Solution to p. 88

TWENTY QUESTIONS IN THE TAVERN

The spice merchant and his son were aboard a sailing-ship heading for the Indies, where they were to take on provisions. The ship was attacked by pirates and sunk, leaving only the merchant and the ship's cook alive.

These two were washed up on a desert island and survived as best they could. Every day the cook prepared a meagre meal from, he told the merchant, cormorant.

After six months living on this diet, they were finally rescued and brought back to land.

The spice merchant was passing the tavern and happened to see that cormorant was the chef's special, so he ordered it. But the dish did not taste the same as the one given to him by the cook on the desert island.

At that moment the merchant realised that the cook had lied to him and that he had made their meals from the flesh of those who had not survived the shipwreck: the merchant must undoubtedly therefore have eaten his own son, and that is why he cried so bitterly over his plate ...

Solution to p. 89

UPERSTITION

Nostradamus was mistaken: the new year can never begin on Friday the thirteenth, since it always begins on January the first!

Solution to p. 90

CHAINWORK

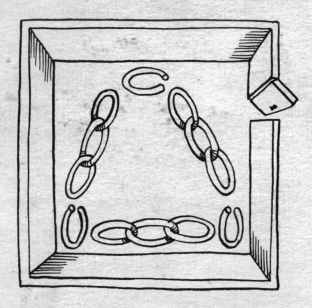

The trick is to break the three links of one piece, which will cost 15 farthings.

It will then take three solderings to join the other three pieces, which will cost 30 farthings. In total therefore, Lord Aubrey will have spent 15 + 30, or 45 farthings.

Solution to p. 91

 ACKWARDS AND
FORWARDS

Turn on the first switch and wait five minutes.

Next, turn off the first switch, and turn on the second. Then go immediately up to the attic:

-- if the bulb is alight, it must be connected to the second switch;

-- if the bulb is not alight but it is hot, then it was the first switch that turned it on;

-- if the bulb is not alight and is cold, it must be connected to the third switch.

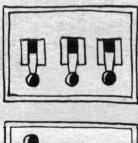

Solution to p. 92

WHAT AM I?

I am an Envelope.

IVE TRIANGLES

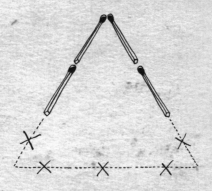

becomes:

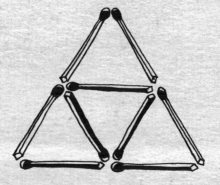

So there is one big triangle, and four small ones.

Solution to p. 94

 OUR TRIANGLES

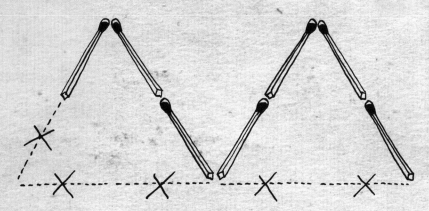

becomes:

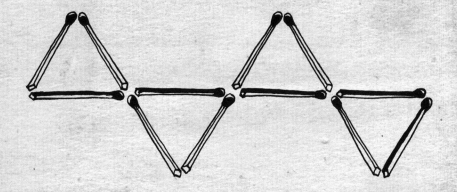

GLASS PYRAMID

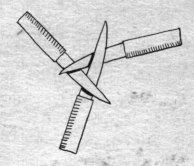

All they have to do is position the knives as follows and stand the fourth glass on top:

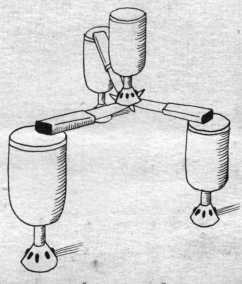

Solution to p. 96

TEN FINGERS MAKE NINE

All you have to do is count on your fingers!

For example, to multiply 9 X 5, just bend the fifth finger, which is on your left hand, and then " read " your fingers. There are four straight fingers to the left of your bent finger - they correspond to the tens - and five straight fingers to the right of the bent finger - these are the units: the answer is therefore 45.

Try it with 9 X 6: this time bend the sixth finger, which is on your right hand. There are five straight fingers to the left of your bent finger - the tens - and four to the right - the units: so the answer is 54.

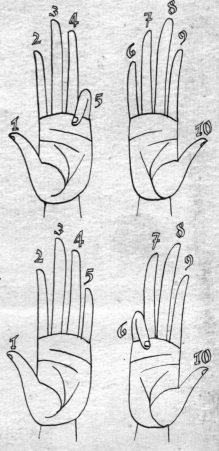

Solution to p. 97

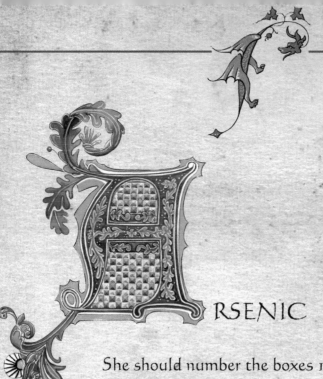

ARSENIC

She should number the boxes 1 to 12 from left to right, and then take:
-- 1 pill from box 1;
-- 2 pills from box 2;
-- 3 pills from box 3;
etc.
-- 12 pills from box 12.

Then she should weigh all the pills from the 12 boxes, ie 78 in all. If all the pills were harmless, they would weigh: 78 pills X 10 mg = 780 mg.

Given that one arsenic pill weighs 1 mg less, she just has to calculate the difference. For example, if the queen finds the total weight to be 777 mg, then it will be box number 3 (from which she removed 3 pills) that contains the arsenic.

The only thing the mistress has to count ... are the days she has left!

Solution to p. 98

 HECK MATES

Simple: Thibaud and Clothaire weren't playing each other!

RESTORING THE EQUATION

There are two possible solutions:

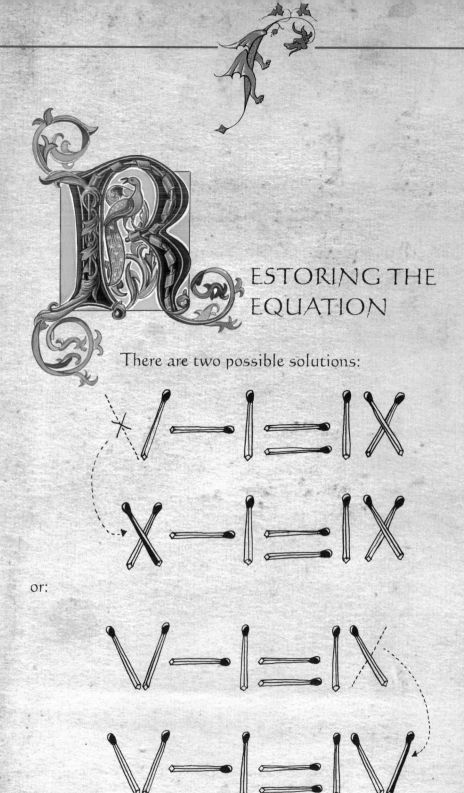

or:

Solution to p. 100

THREE PILES

This trick uses 27 cards.
There are three piles on the table.

-- The first time your friend tells you which pile their card is in, place that pile in between the other two piles and put them all together into one pile. Then make your three piles again, this time placing the cards one by one on each pile in turn (left pile first, then the middle, then the right, then the left again, the middle, the right, etc).
-- The second time your friend tells you which pile their card is in, put that pile under the other two, and lay them out again as above.
-- The third time they tell you which pile it is in, put that pile in between the others again.

The last part of the trick takes care of itself.

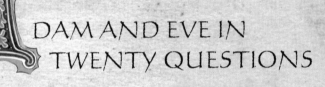ADAM AND EVE IN TWENTY QUESTIONS

He sees that the two bodies have no navel and can therefore only have been born from nothing!

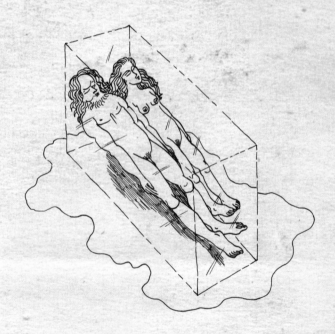

Solution to p. 102

OTTERING ON THE TIGHTROPE

The pole doesn't fall at all!

What happens is, his hands will meet in the middle of the pole, which will therefore stay in equilibrium.

Surprising, wouldn't you agree?

Solution to p. 103

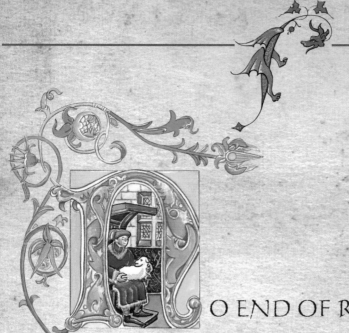

O END OF RECTANGLES

There are 30 rectangles on the floor of the throne room:

-- 8 rectangles that are 1 X 1;
-- 6 rectangles that are 1 X 2;
-- 4 rectangles that are 2 X 1;
-- 4 rectangles that are 1 X 3;
-- 3 rectangles that are 2 X 2;
-- 2 rectangles that are 1 X 4;
-- 2 rectangles that are 2 X 3;
-- and 1 rectangle that is 2 X 4.

30

Solution to p. 104

THE FIFTEEN DOORS

Here's one possible route:

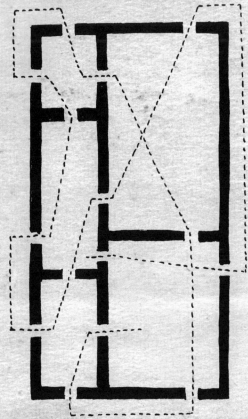

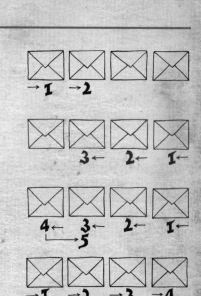

ENVELOPES

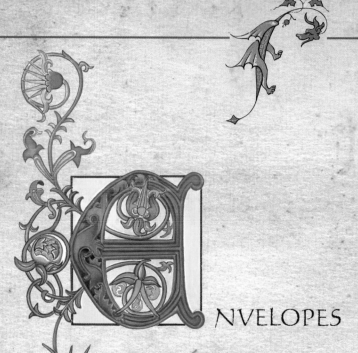

Your secret is that you will always choose the second envelope from the left. This is how it works:

-- if your friend throws a 2, take the second envelope from the left;
-- if they throw a 3, count 1, 2, 3 but starting from the right;
-- if they throw a 5, count 1, 2, 3, 4, 5 starting from the right, and doubling back from the left;
-- if they throw a 6, count 1, 2, 3, 4, 5, 6 starting from the left, and doubling back from the right;
-- if they throw a 1, just take one envelope away (the first on the left) and open the second one;
-- and if they throw a 4, which starts with an F, call out A, B, C, D, E, F starting from the left, and doubling back from the right.

Solution to p. 106

OUNTING WITH LETTERS

$$17$$
$$\times \quad 4$$
$$68$$
$$+ \, 25$$
$$93$$

Solution to p. 107

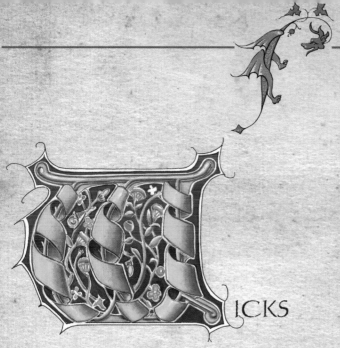

WICKS

First of all, Merlin lights ends A, B and C, all at the same time.

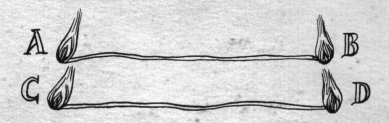

When the first wick (AB) has burnt down completely, 30 minutes will have passed and at this point he lights end D ...

... and the 30 minutes remaining on the second wick (CD) will burn down in 15 minutes: 30 min + 15 min = 45 min.

Solution to p. 108

 IVE SQUARES

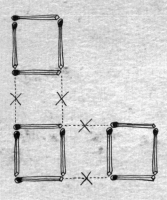

becomes:

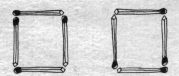

IVE SQUARES PART 2

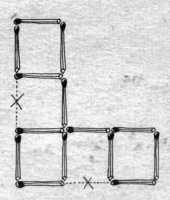

becomes:

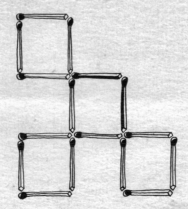

Solution to p. 110

OUNCERS

No glass, even a crystal one, will bounce once it's broken! That's why it shatters on the last bounce.

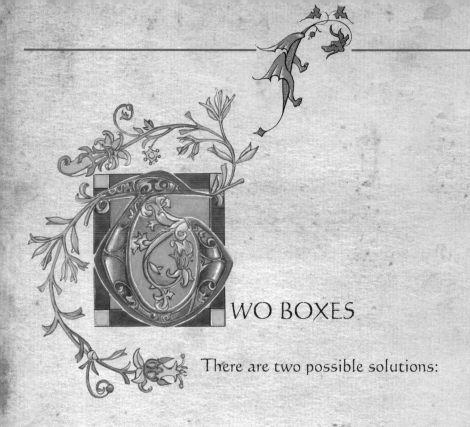

WO BOXES

There are two possible solutions:

Put one diamond in the
smaller box. In the larger box,
put the two remaining
diamonds AND the first box.

Or:

Put the three diamonds in
the smaller box, and put that
box in the larger box.

Solution to p. 112

ONE BOOK, ONE PAGE

Make an accordion fold in the sheet of parchment; it will then be able to support the weight of the book.

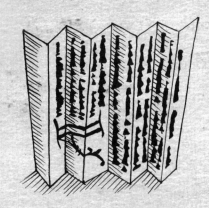

IVE CIRCLES

Here is one possible solution:

The sum of the numbers in each circle is 11.

Solution to p. 114

 EADS OR TAILS

Here are three possible solutions:

# OMBUSTION

Put a handful of coarse salt in glass of water, and mix it well.
Soak half the length of thread in the salt water, and then let it dry.
Make a note of which end was in the water; that's the one you can set
light to without it burning to the point of breaking.

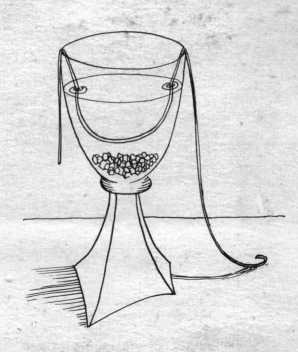

Solution to p. 116

WET PAINT

40 sides would be numbered: 7 in front, 7 at the back, 7 facing left, 7 facing right, 6 on top and 6 underneath.

 URDEROUS ROUTE

He returns to his own cell after the first murder - there is no corpse there - and then takes the following route ...

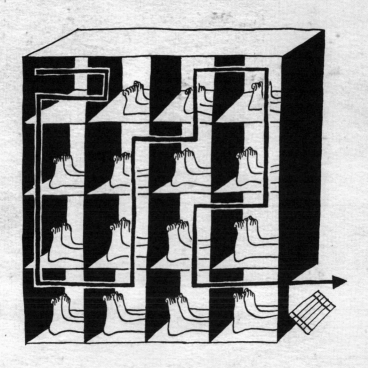

Solution to p. 118

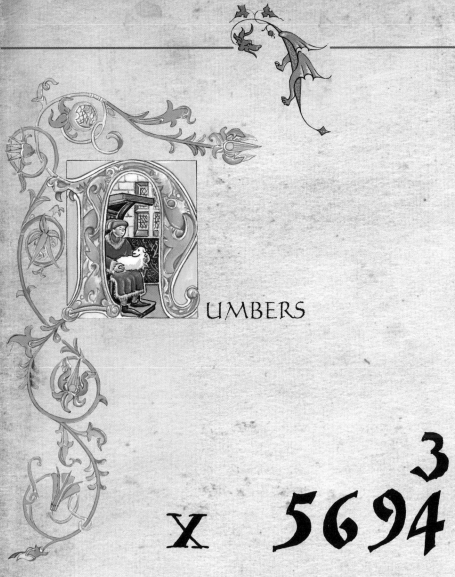

UMBERS

$$x \quad 569\overset{3}{4}$$
$$\overline{17082}$$

HOLE FULL OF STARCH

Take a straw and using your index finger, block off one end.
Hold it at a perpendicular to the potato and with a sharp
tap, drive the straw into it and through.

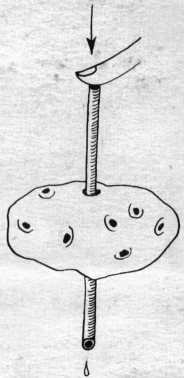

Solution to p. 160

 INES AND COLUMNS

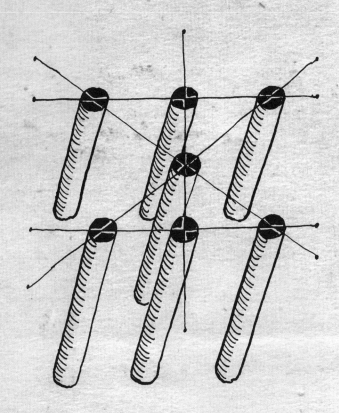

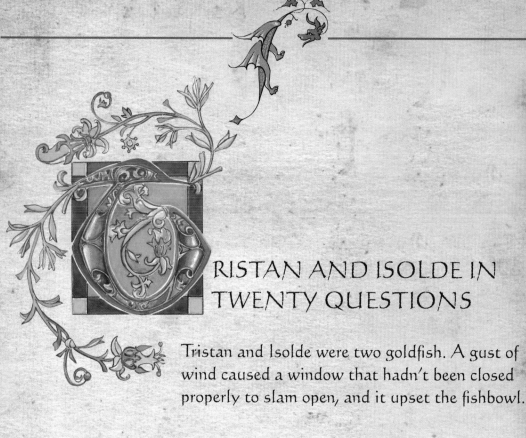

CRISTAN AND ISOLDE IN TWENTY QUESTIONS

Tristan and Isolde were two goldfish. A gust of wind caused a window that hadn't been closed properly to slam open, and it upset the fishbowl.

Solution p. 122

HREE QUEENS

The card in the middle will inevitably be the queen of hearts.

 EHICLES

While the bicycle is moving, it is as if the cart is standing still while the bicycle is moving at 15 kmh (the difference between the two speeds).

So when the bicycle stops, the cart, which is moving at 45 kmh, will travel the same distance three times faster than the bicycle. The bicycle must therefore travel for fifteen minutes (3 X 5 minutes stopped) since 45 equals 3 times 15 kmh.

Solution to p. 124

 ESTORING THE EQUATION 2

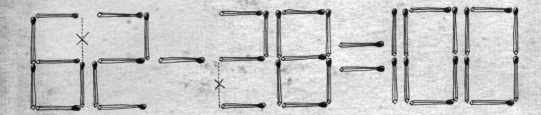

becomes:

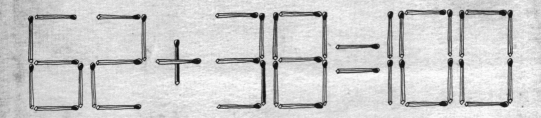

REEDOM

With the ring facing you, as well as the two ends of the cord, take hold of the ring and pull it off. It will come free of the cord (figure D).

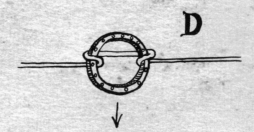

D

On the other hand, if you pull the ring while the ends of the cord are facing your friend, it will remain firmly bound (figure E).

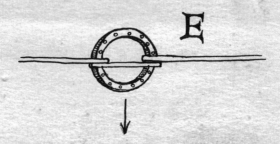

E

Solution to p. 126

ALIMINATION

20 =	7	5̶	5	3̶	6	2
20 =	8	1	7̶	6	5	1̶
20 =	5̶	8	4	3̶	4	5
20 =	4	6	8	1	2	9̶
20 =	1	2̶	8	4	7	8
20 =	6̶	5	3	7	4̶	5

|| || || || || ||

20 20 20 20 20 20

Solution to p. 127

ONFETTI

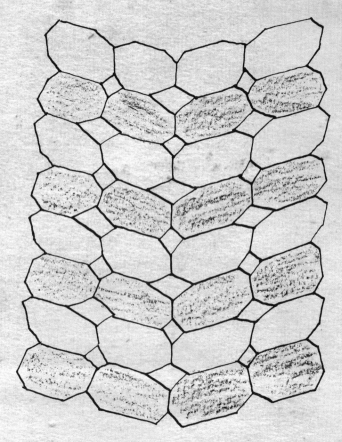

There would be 21 holes.

Solution to p. 128

LOVE POTION

Let A be the empty 3 fl oz flask, B the empty 5 fl oz flask, and C the full 8 fl oz flask.

To measure 4 fl oz, Merlin:
1. fills flask A with the contents of flask C;
2. pours the contents of flask A into flask B;
3. again fills flask A from flask C;
4. uses flask A to fill flask B, then discards what is left in flask A;
5. pours the contents of flask B into flask A;
6. fills flask C with the what is left in flask B.

There is now 4 fl oz of toad oil in flask C.

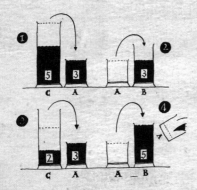

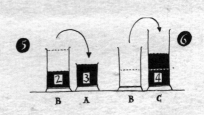

NVERSION DIVERSION

First of all, turn cards A, C and D.

Then turn cards A, B and C.

Then turn cards B, C and D.

Finally, turn cards A, B and D.

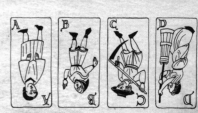

Solution to p. 130

 NN-SUFFICIENT SPACE

When the innkeeper puts the eleventh troubadour in Room 10, there is still a twelfth person who is waiting to be accommodated. The wording of the riddle is misleading!

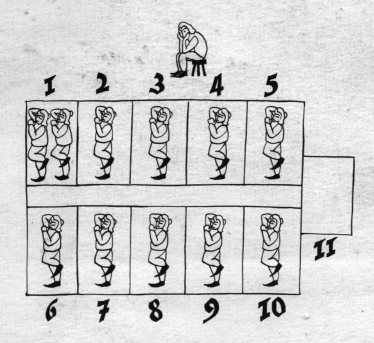

THE EARTH IS ROUND

You would only need another 6.28 m of rope.
The radius of the larger circle round the Earth
would increase by 1 m, ie the height of one pole.
And the radius of a circle is 2 × π × r.
So if the radius increases by 1 m, the new
circumference will increase by 2 × π × r,
ie 2 × 3.14 × 1 = 6.28.

6,28 m

Solution to p. 132

WHY MAKE FIVE WHEN YOU CAN MAKE NINE?

becomes:

Thus he gets 7 small squares, and 2 large ones.

Solution to p. 133

PUNCTURE-PROOF

All he has to do is to pass the knitting needle, preferably oiled, through the two thickest areas of the balloon. The needle will pierce the balloon without it bursting or deflating.

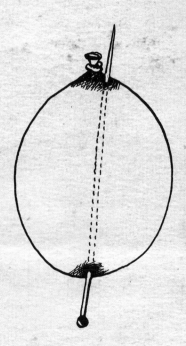

Solution to p. 134

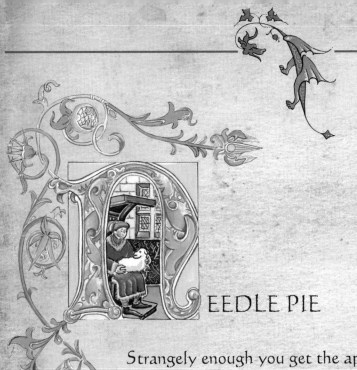

NEEDLE PIE

Strangely enough you get the approximate value of π!
The higher the number of needles dropped, the closer the
result is to π.

So with 100 needles you should get 31 needles crossing a
line, in which case π = 100 ÷ 31 = 3.2258.

With 1,000 needles, you should get 317 needles crossing a
line, in which case π = 1,000 ÷ 317 = 3.1545.

Solution to p. 135

ANGLE OF A CUBE

Imagine a similar line drawn on the hidden side of the cube. That would make a triangle, in which, being equilateral, every angle will be 60°.

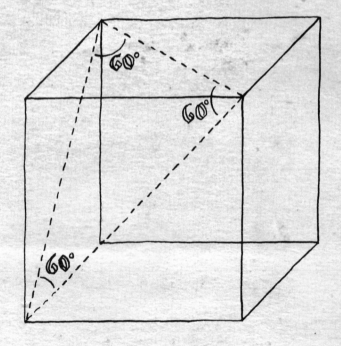

Solution to p. 136

TWENTY QUESTIONS IN THE DESERT

He was part of the crew of a flying machine. The machine was in danger of crashing and there was an urgent need to get rid of some ballast. Everyone on board therefore got rid of their clothes but the flying machine was still too heavy, so they decided to draw straws to see who should make the ultimate sacrifice.

The loser, naked and still holding the straw, was obliged to jump from the flying machine and landed in the desert, where he was killed on the spot!

Solution to p. 137

OW HARD DO WE
REALLY WORK?

The weekends, holidays and Bank Holidays should have been subtracted
before the total was divided by three.

Solution to p. 138

ULLSEYE

Angus hit the target six times.

Number of knives in hand		Number of knives in hand	Knives won	Number of knives left to throw
5	–	1	+2	6
6	–	1	+2	7
7	–	1	+2	8
8	–	1	+2	9
9	–	1	+2	10
10	–	1	+2	11
Total		6		

Having hit the target six times and thus thrown six knives, he has eleven more knives to throw. He must therefore have missed the target with these every time.

Solution to p. 139

DOOR TO DOOR

The question the prisoner should ask just one guard is:
" Which door would the other guard tell me was the way out? "

He should then go through whichever door the guard did not indicate.

One other possible solution would be to ask:

" Is the one who tells the truth standing in front of the door that leads out? "

If the answer is yes, the prisoner should choose the door with the guard of whom he asked the question; if it is no, then he should choose the other door and so freedom.

Solution to p. 140

 ROM RECTANGLE TO SQUARE

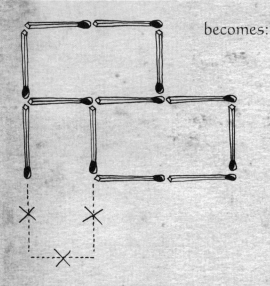

becomes:

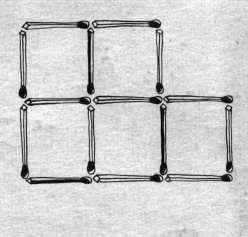

Thus we have five small squares and one large one.

Solution to p. 141

 ROM RECTANGLE TO SQUARE 2

There are two possible solutions:

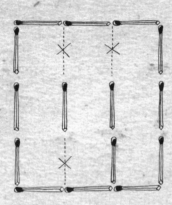

or:

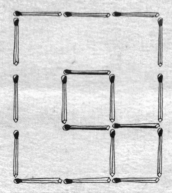

Solution to p. 142

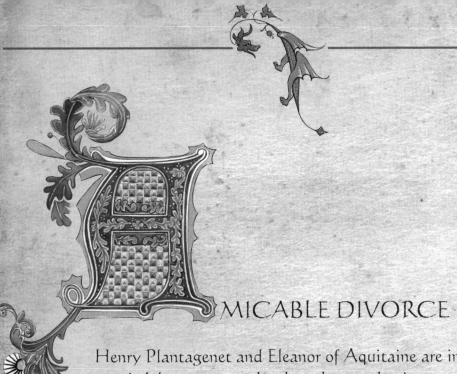

AMICABLE DIVORCE

Henry Plantagenet and Eleanor of Aquitaine are indeed
married, but not to each other; they are having an affair.

Solution to p. 143

 IND THE NUMBER

All I do is add the numbers in the top left hand of each card indicated, and that will give me the number in question.

For example, say the number chosen is 44; it appears on cards C, D and F. If I add up the first numbers on those cards, I get:

4 + 8 + 32 = 44.

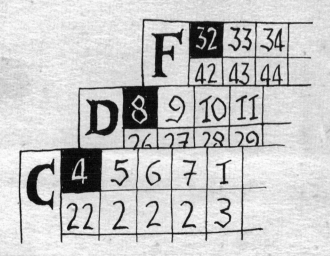

Solution to p. 144

 INESWEEPER

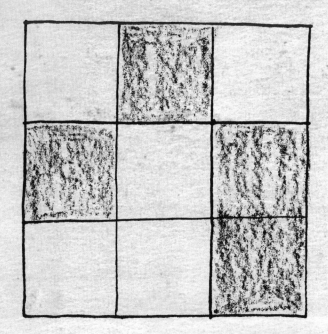

AX YOU CAN EAT

The provost's candles are in fact edible.

Using an apple-corer, the castle's pastry chef extracts a cylindrical piece of fruit which looks just like a candle. Then he takes a shelled walnut and shapes it to look like a wick, placing it on top of the candle. Once lit, the nut will burn like a real wick!

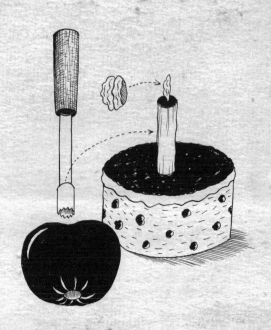

Solution to p. 146

ARGE FAMILY

The customers are a man and his sister, together with their respective children, one a boy and the other a girl.

THE NAUGHTY MONK

Brother Stephen takes a double sheet of parchment and places it flat on that part of the ruler which rests on the table. Henceforth, a tap on the end will no longer send the ruler flying, and if the annoying Brother Gontran continues to try to launch his ruler by tapping it harder, he risks breaking it whereas the parchment won't be damaged at all.

Solution to p. 148

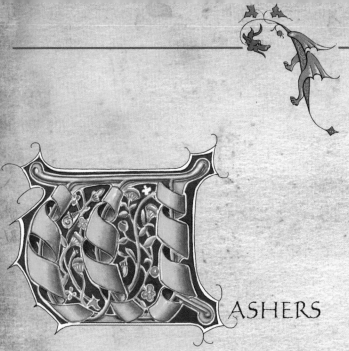

WASHERS

Under the napkin, lift the washers to free up the first one, the one with the loop running through it. Just pull the loop and the washer will come off easily. Now you can slide off the remaining four washers. Put the first washer back over the loop by reversing the process and then remove the napkin.

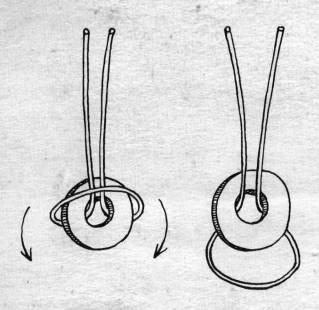

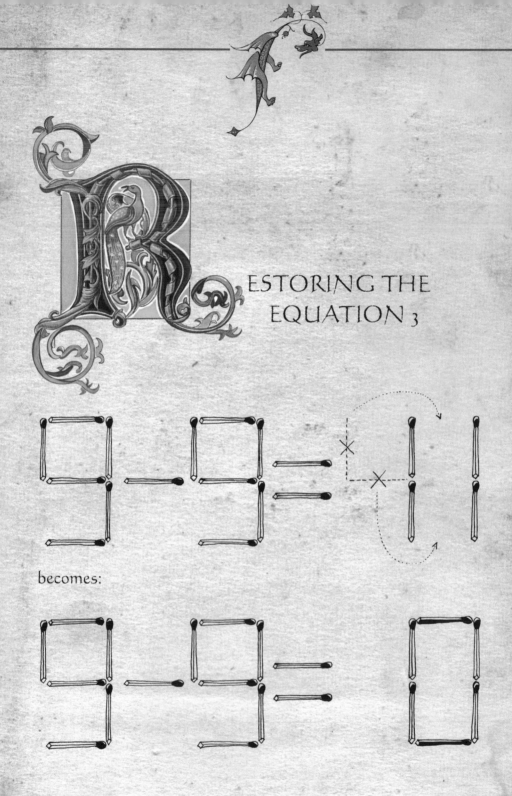

RESTORING THE EQUATION 3

becomes:

Solution to p. 150

PARADOX

The pupil is wrong.

If he wins the case, he may not have to pay Maimonides in accordance with the judgement, but he will have to pay according to the terms of their arrangement.

If Maimonides wins, the pupil may not have to pay according to the terms of their arrangement, but he will have to pay in accordance with the decision of the court.

In both cases therefore he will have to pay his teacher!

Solution to p. 151

 **RUIT SALAD**

No, the knife has no magic powers!

This trick requires a little preparation: to slice the banana without peeling it, stick a needle in through the skin and move it from side to side as shown. The holes left by the needle will be invisible.

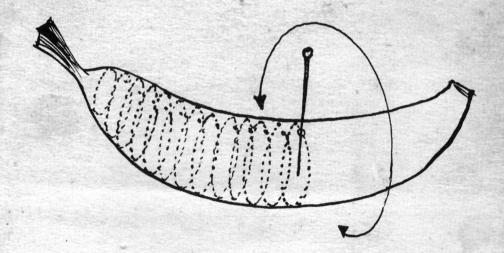

Solution to p. 152

TWENTY QUESTIONS IN THE FOREST

While the man was diving in a lake, a forest fire broke out nearby. A fire-fighting flying boat came to pick up water and accidentally scooped up the diver at the same time, subsequently releasing its cargo over the fire.

ARCHIMEDES

In accordance with Archimedes' Principle, the boat undergoes an upward thrust equal to the weight of the volume of displaced water. The boat's anchor thus displaces a volume of water equal to its weight. However, once the anchor is underwater, it only displaces its own volume.

The water level will therefore fall.

Solution to p. 154

ATE-KEEPER

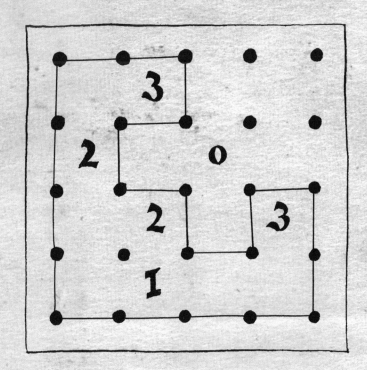

FAIR TRADE

Dame Cunégonde and Dame Hermance and Dame Ermangarde share eight dishes in all. Therefore, each has eaten 8/3 of the food.

Dame Hermance, having brought three dishes, has only given away one third of a dish to the person who brought nothing.

Dame Cunégonde, who brought five dishes, has given away seven thirds of her food to Dame Ermangarde.

Consequently the money should be distributed as follows:
--   1 groat for Dame Hermance who brought three dishes;
--   7 groats for Dame Cunégonde, who brought five dishes.